THE NATIVE AMERICAN STORY BOOK

Stories Of The American Indians For Children

Written And Edited By
G.W. Mullins
With Original Art By
C.L. Hause

LIGHT OF THE MOON PUBLISHING

ISBN: 978-1-64007-709-6

Second Edition Printing

Light Of The Moon Publishing has allowed this work to remain
exactly as the author intended, verbatim, without editorial input.

Printed in the United States of America

The following book represents a collection of Native American
works which are public domain. You may have read the stories
before. In true story telling fashion, the stories have been left as
close to the original form as possible. In Native American
culture, in order to pass the stories along with all information
intact, they had to be told pretty much word for word, to keep the
legends alive. Many of these stories were translated directly
from original Native language texts. With that in mind, please
be aware that some spellings and word usage may vary from one
tribe to another. For instance, the spelling of "teepee", as used
in this book, can also be written as "tipi", and "tepee". All are
correct. Also when using words like "someone", in most native
cultures, it would be "some one". So keep in mind, these are not
necessarily misspellings. They are simply dialect and
translations.

Other Titles Available From G.W. Mullins And C.L. Hause
Walking With Spirits Native American Myths, Legends, And Folklore
Volumes One Thru Six

The Native American Cookbook

Native American Cooking - An Indian Cookbook With Legends And Folklore

The Native American Story Book - Stories Of The American Indians For Children
Volumes One Thru Five

The Best Native American Stories For Children

Cherokee A Collection of American Indian Legends, Stories And Fables

Creation Myths - Tales Of The Native American Indians

Strange Tales Of The Native American Indians

Spirit Quest - Stories Of The Native American Indians

Animal Tales Of The Native American Indians

Medicine Man - Shamanism, Natural Healing, Remedies And Stories Of The Native
American Indians

Native American Legends: Stories Of The Hopi Indians
Volumes One and Two

Totem Animals Of The Native Americans

The Best Native American Myths, Legends And Folklore
Volumes One Thru Three

Ghosts, Spirits And The Afterlife In Native American Indian Mythology And
Folklore

The Native American Art Book – Art Inspired By Native American Myths And
Legends

For information about the book and novel releases of
G.W. Mullins please visit his web site at
http://gwmullins.wix.com/officialsite

All images contained in this book are original works by
C.L. Hause. For more information on his art and other projects
please visit his web page at *http://clarencehause.wix.com/homepage*

THE NATIVE AMERICAN STORY COLLECTION SERIES

Featuring The Writing Of Best-Selling Author

G.W. MULLINS

And Original Art From Award Winning Artist C.L. HAUSE

The Native American Story Book Series / The Best Native American Stories For Children

Tales Of The Native American Indians / Native American Legends Series

Walking With Spirits Volumes 1 thru 6
Native American Myths, Legends, And Folklore

The Native American Cookbook

The Best Native American Stories for Children

Native American Cooking
An Indian Cookbook With Legends And Folklore

The Native American Story Book Volumes 1 thru 5
Stories Of The American Indians For Children

Creation Myths - Tales Of The Native American Indians

Strange Tales Of The Native American Indians

Animal Tales Of The Native American Indians

Spirit Quest Native American Indian Legends Stories and Fables

Medicine Man - Shamanism, Natural Healing, Remedies And Stories Of The Native American Indians

Cherokee A Collection of American Indian Legends, Stories And Fables

Native American Legends: Stories Of The Hopi Indians Volumes One and Two

The Native American Art Book

The Best Native American Myths, Legends And Folklore Vols 1-5

Ghosts, Spirits And The Afterlife In Native American Indian Mythology And Folklore

Native American Cooking, Art And Medicine Books

Walking With Spirits Native American Myths, Legends, And Folklore Series

The Best Native American Native American Myths, Legends And Folklore

LIGHT OF DE MOON PUBLISHING

This book is dedicated to Vince Mullins, my Grandfather (Pawpaw). He was a tall red man with fire in his eyes… who I loved so much.

G.W. Mullins

"May the stars carry your sadness away,
May the flowers fill your heart with beauty,
May hope forever wipe away your tears,
And, above all, may silence make you strong."

~ Chief Dan George

Chief Dan George, (July 24, 1899 – September 23, 1981) was a chief of the Tsleil-Waututh Nation, a Coast Salish band located on Burrard Inlet in North Vancouver, British Columbia, Canada. He was also an author, poet, actor, and an Officer of the Order of Canada. At the age of 71, he was nominated for an Academy Award for Best Supporting Actor in Little Big Man.

Table Of Contents

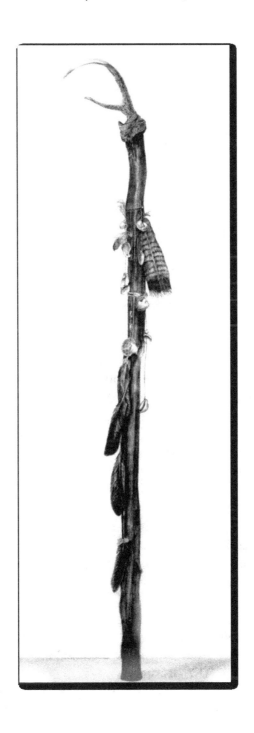

Introduction

For many hundreds of years, people wandered into the great northwest. They came from all directions across Canada and the United States. These early people were not only skilled farmers, they were also clever builders, engineers, and weavers. They loved games of skill. They created stories, songs and poetry. Although they spoke many different languages, and had many different customs, they had at least one thing in common - they were the first immigrants.

These people lived in the United States long before the arrival of Christopher Columbus and the Europeans. These people and cultures are called Native Americans. The first people to live in a land are called indigenous peoples. This means they were the original settlers. The Native Americans are the indigenous peoples and cultures of the United States.

So why are these peoples referred to as Indians or American Indians? This is because when Columbus had first landed in America, he thought he had sailed all the way to the country of India. He called the locals Indians and the name stuck for some time.

The Native Americans were grouped into tribes or nations usually based on the area they lived in and their culture such as their religion, customs, and language. Sometimes smaller tribes were part of a bigger tribe or nation. There were hundreds of tribes throughout the United States when

Columbus first arrived. Many of them are well known such as the Cherokee, Apache, and the Navajo.

Native Americans used games, myths, dance, and impersonation to teach the children of their history and ways of life. They did not write down or record their history, so we have to find out about their history in other ways. Many oral histories were lost when European explorers and settlers came to the Americas. With them, they brought disease. The People became ill with smallpox and other illnesses. Many died. Much was lost.

Today, there are over 500 federally recognized tribes in the United States alone. We can learn from traditions and stories that have been passed down from generation to generation within the remaining tribes.

Through storytelling, the rich history of the Native American tribes is alive and well today. It has been shared and preserved and still pays tribute to fallen heroes of the past. It is through these glimpses into the past, and these stories much like the ones that are contained in this book, that you can see what a proud heritage they possess and how in tune with the Earth Native Americans really are.

With this book I hope you understand the Native American people a little better and understand where they have come from and what they can offer the world. By exploring these stories I offer you a glimpse into an often forgotten past. The past of my people. I was born Cherokee and as a child heard many of these stories. These stories were passed to me in the old traditional way by my grandfather. And now I give these stories to you, to carry forward for younger generations to explore and learn.

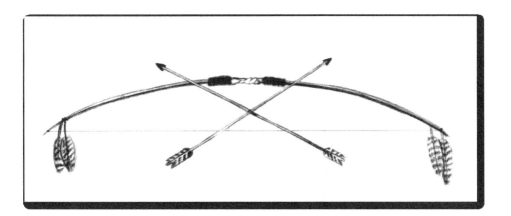

The Magic Arrows

There was once a young man who wanted to go on a journey. His mother provided him with sacks of dried meat and pairs of moccasins, but his father said to him:

"Here, my son, are four magic arrows. When you are in need, shoot one of them!"

The young man went forth alone, and hunted in the forest for many days. Usually he was successful, but a day came when he was hungry and could not find meat. Then he sent forth one of the magic arrows, and at the end of the day there lay a fat Bear with the arrow in his side. The hunter cut out the tongue for his meal, and of the body of the Bear he made a thank-offering to the Great Mystery.

Again he was in need, and again in the morning he shot a magic arrow, and at nightfall beside his camp-fire he found an Elk lying with the arrow in his heart. Once more he ate the tongue and offered up the body as a sacrifice. The third time he killed a Moose with his arrow, and the fourth time a Buffalo.

After the fourth arrow had been spent, the young man came one day out of the forest, and before him there lay a great circular village of skin lodges. At one side, and some little way from the rest of the people, he noticed a small and poor tent where an old couple lived all alone. At the edge of the wood he took off his clothes and hid them in a hollow tree. Then, touching the top of his head with his staff, he turned himself into a little ragged boy and went toward the poor tent.

The old woman saw him coming, and said to her old man: "Old man, let us keep this little boy for our own! He seems to be a fine, bright-eyed little fellow, and we are all alone."

"What are you thinking of, old woman?" grumbled the old man. "We can hardly keep ourselves, and yet you talk of taking in a ragged little scamp from nobody knows where!"

In the meantime the boy had come quite near, and the old wife beckoned to him to enter the lodge.

"Sit down, my grandson, sit down!" she said, kindly; and, in spite of the old man's black looks, she handed him a small dish of parched corn, which was all the food they had.

The boy ate and stayed on. By and by he said to the old woman: "Grandmother, I should like to have grandfather make me some arrows!"

"You hear, my old man?" said she. "It will be very well for you to make some little arrows for the boy."

"And why should I make arrows for a strange little ragged boy?" grumbled the old man.

However, he made two or three, and the boy went hunting. In a short time he returned with several small birds. The old woman took them and pulled off the feathers, thanking him and praising him as she did so. She quickly made the little birds into soup, of which the old man ate gladly, and with the soft feathers she stuffed a small pillow.

"You have done well, my grandson!" he said; for they were really very poor.

Not long after, the boy said to his adopted grandmother: "Grandmother, when you see me at the edge of the wood yonder, you must call out: 'A Bear! there goes a Bear!' "

This she did, and the boy again sent forth one of the magic arrows, which he had taken from the body of his game and kept by him. No sooner had he shot, than he saw the same Bear that he had offered up, lying before him with the arrow in his side!

Now there was great rejoicing in the lodge of the poor old couple. While they were out skinning the Bear and cutting the meat in thin strips to dry, the boy sat alone in the lodge. In the pot on the fire was the Bear's tongue, which he wanted for himself.

All at once a young girl stood in the doorway. She drew her robe modestly before her face as she said in a low voice:

"I come to borrow the mortar of your grandmother!"

The boy gave her the mortar, and also a piece of the tongue which he had cooked, and she went away.

When all of the Bear meat was gone, the boy sent forth a second arrow and killed an Elk, and with the third and fourth he shot the Moose and the Buffalo as before, each time recovering his arrow.

Soon after, he heard that the people of the large village were in trouble. A great Red Eagle, it was said, flew over the village every day at dawn, and the people believed that it was a bird of evil omen, for they no longer had any success in hunting. None of their braves had been able to shoot the Eagle, and the chief had offered his only daughter in marriage to the man who should kill it.

When the boy heard this, he went out early the next morning and lay in wait for the Red Eagle. At the touch of his magic arrow, it fell at his feet, and the boy pulled out his arrow and went home without speaking to anyone.

But the thankful people followed him to the poor little lodge, and when they had found him, they brought the chief's beautiful daughter to be his wife. Lo, she was the girl who had come to borrow his grandmother's mortar!

Then he went back to the hollow tree where his clothes were hidden, and came back a handsome young man, richly dressed for his wedding.

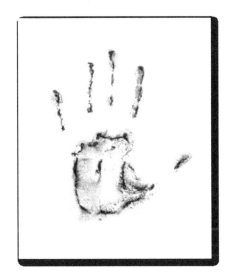

Origin of the Pleiades

(An Onondaga Legend)

A long time ago a party of Indians went through the woods toward a good hunting-ground, which they had long known. They traveled several days through a very wild country, going on leisurely and camping by the way.

At last they reached Kan-ya-ti-yo, "the beautiful lake," where the gray rocks were crowned with great forest trees. Fish swarmed in the waters, and at every jutting point the deer came down from the hills around to bathe or drink of the lake. On the hills and in the valleys were huge beech and chestnut trees, where squirrels chattered, and bears came to take their morning and evening meals.

The chief of the band was Hah-yah-no, "Tracks in the water," and he halted his party on the lake shore that he might return thanks to the Great Spirit for their safe arrival at this good hunting-ground. "Here will we build our lodges for the winter, and may the Great Spirit, who has prospered us on our way, send us plenty of game, and health and peace." The Indian is always thankful.

The pleasant autumn days passed on. The lodges had been built, and hunting had prospered, when the children took a fancy to dance for their own amusement. They were getting lonesome, having little to do, and so they met daily in a quiet spot by the lake to have what they called their jolly dance. They had done this a long time, when one day a very old man came to them. They had seen no one like him before. He was dressed in white feathers, and his white hair shone like silver. His appearance was strange, his words were unpleasant as well. He told them they must stop their dancing, or evil would happen to them. Little did the children heed, for they were intent on their sport, and again and again the old man appeared, repeating his warning.

The mere dances did not afford all the enjoyment the children wished, and a little boy, who liked a good dinner, suggested a feast the next time they met. The food must come from their parents, and all were asked when they returned home. "You will waste and spoil good victuals," said one. "You can eat at home as you should," said another, and so they got nothing at all. Sorry as they were for this, they met and danced as before. A little to eat after each dance would have made them happy indeed. Empty stomachs cause no joy.

One day, as they danced, they found themselves rising little by little into the air, their heads being light through hunger. How this happened they did not know, but one said, "Do not look back, for something strange is taking place." A woman, saw them rise, and called them back, but with no effect, for they still rose slowly above the earth. She ran to the camp, and all rushed out with food of every kind, but the children would not return, though their parents called piteously after them. When one would look back he became a falling star. The others reached the sky, and are now what we call the Pleiades, and the Onondagas Oot-kwa-tah. Every falling or shooting star recalls the story, but the seven stars shine on continuously, a pretty band of dancing children.

Even the seasons form a great circle in their changing, and always come back again to where they were. The life of a person is a circle from childhood to childhood, and so it is in everything where power moves.

Black Elk

Grandmother Spider Steals the Fire *(Choctaw)*

A Story of the Choctaw People of Tennessee and Mississippi

The Choctaw People say that when the People first came up out of the ground, People were encased in cocoons, their eyes closed, their limbs folded tightly to their bodies. And this was true of all People, the Bird People, the Animal

People, the Insect People, and the Human People. The Great Spirit took pity on them and sent down someone to unfold their limbs, dry them off, and open their eyes. But the opened eyes saw nothing, because the world was dark, no sun, no moon, not even any stars.

All the People moved around by touch, and if they found something that didn't eat them first, they ate it raw, for they had no fire to cook it. All the People met in a great powwow, with the Animal and Bird People taking the lead, and the Human People hanging back. The Animal and Bird People decided that life was not good, but cold and miserable. A solution must be found! Someone spoke from the dark, "I have heard that the people in the East have fire." This caused a stir of wonder, "What could fire be?" There was a general discussion, and it was decided that if, as rumor had it, fire was warm and gave light, they should have it too. Another voice said, "But the people of the East are too greedy to share with us," So it was decided that the Bird and Animal People should steal what they needed, the fire!

But, who should have the honor? Grandmother Spider volunteered, "I can do it! Let me try!" But at the same time, Opossum began to speak. "I, Opossum, am a great chief of the animals. I will go to the East and since I am a great hunter, I will take the fire and hide it in the bushy hair on my tail." It was well know that Opossum had the furriest tail of all the animals, so he was selected.

When Opossum came to the East, he soon found the beautiful, red fire, jealously guarded by the people of the East. But Opossum got closer and closer until he picked up a small piece of burning wood, and stuck it in the hair of his tail, which promptly began to smoke, then flame. The people of the East said, "Look, that Opossum has stolen our fire!" They took it and put it back where it came from and drove Opossum away. Poor Opossum! Every bit of hair had burned from his tail, and to this day, opossums have no hair at all on their tails.

Once again, the powwow had to find a volunteer chief. Grandmother Spider again said, "Let me go! I can do it!" But this time a bird was elected, Buzzard. Buzzard was very proud. "I can succeed where Opossum has failed. I will fly to the East on my great wings, then hide the stolen fire in the beautiful long feathers on my head." The birds and animals still did not understand the nature of fire. So Buzzard flew to the East on his powerful wings, swooped past those defending the fire, picked up a small piece of burning ember, and hid it in his head feathers. Buzzard's head began to smoke and flame even faster! The people of the East said, "Look! Buzzard has stolen the fire!" And they took it and put it back where it came from.

Poor Buzzard! His head was now bare of feathers, red and blistered looking. And to this day, buzzards have naked heads that are bright red and blistered.

The powwow now sent Crow to look the situation over, for Crow was very clever. Crow at that time was pure white, and had the sweetest singing voice of all the birds. But he took so long standing over the fire, trying to find the perfect piece to steal that his white feathers were smoked black. And he breathed so much smoke that when he tried to sing, out came a harsh, "Caw! Caw!"

The Council said, "Opossum has failed. Buzzard and Crow have failed. Who shall we send?"

Tiny Grandmother Spider shouted with all her might, "LET ME TRY IT PLEASE!"

Though the council members thought Grandmother Spider had little chance of success, it was agreed that she should have her turn. Grandmother Spider looked then like she looks now, she had a small torso suspended by two sets of legs that turned the other way. She walked on all of her wonderful legs toward a stream where she had found clay. With those legs, she made a tiny clay container and a lid that fit perfectly with a tiny notch for air in the corner of the lid. Then she put the container on her back, spun a web all the way to the East, and walked tiptoe until she came to the fire. She was so small, the people from the East took no notice. She took a tiny piece of fire, put it in the container, and covered it with the lid. Then she walked back on tiptoe along the web until she came to the People. Since they couldn't see any fire, they said, "Grandmother Spider has failed."

"Oh no," she said, "I have the fire!" She lifted the pot from her back, and the lid from the pot, and the fire flamed up into its friend, the air. All the Birds and Animal People began to decide who would get this wonderful warmth. Bear said, "I'll take it!" but then he burned his paws on it and decided fire was not for animals, for look what happened to Opossum!

The Birds wanted no part of it, as Buzzard and Crow were still nursing their wounds. The insects thought it was pretty, but they, too, stayed far away from the fire.

Then a small voice said, "We will take it, if Grandmother Spider will help." The timid humans, whom none of the animals or birds thought much of, were volunteering!

So Grandmother Spider taught the Human People how to feed the fire sticks and wood to keep it from dying, how to keep the fire safe in a circle of stone so it couldn't escape and hurt them or their homes. While she was at it, she taught the humans about pottery made of clay and fire, and about weaving and spinning, at which Grandmother Spider was an expert.

The Choctaw remember. They made a beautiful design to decorate their homes, a picture of Grandmother Spider, two sets of legs up, two down, with a fire symbol on her back. This is so their children never forget to honor Grandmother Spider, Fire-bringer!

The Hunter and Selu

(Cherokee)

[Corn Goddess Tale III]

from James Mooney, *Nineteenth Annual Report of the Bureau of American Ethnology 1897-98*, Part I. (1900)

A hunter had been tramping over the mountains all day long without finding any game and when the sun went down, he built a fire in a hollow stump, swallowed a few mouthfuls of corn gruel and lay down to sleep, tired out and completely discouraged. About the middle of the night he dreamed and seemed to hear the sound of beautiful singing, which continued until near daybreak and then appeared to die away into the upper air.

All next day he hunted with the same poor success, and at night made his lonely camp again, in the woods. He slept and the strange dream came to him again, but so vividly that it seemed to him like an actual happening. Rousing himself before daylight, he still heard the song, and feeling sure now that it was real, he went in the direction of the sound and found that it came from a single green stalk of corn (*selu*). The plant spoke to him, and told him to cut off some of its roots and take them to his home in the settlement, and the next morning to chew them and "go to water" before anyone else was awake, and then to go out again into the woods, and he would kill many deer and from that time on would always be successful in the hunt. The corn plant continued to talk, teaching him hunting secrets and telling him always to be generous with the game he took, until it was noon and the sun was high, when it suddenly took the form of a woman and rose gracefully into the air and was gone from sight, leaving the hunter alone in the woods.

He returned home and told his story, and all the people knew that he had seen Selu, the wife of Kana'tï. He did as the spirit had directed, and from that time was noted as the most successful of all the hunters in the settlement.

The people who are living on this planet need to break with the narrow concept of human liberation, and begin to see liberation as something that needs to be extended to the whole of the natural world. What is needed is the liberation of all things that support life--the air, the water, the trees-- all the things which support the sacred web of life.

from the Haudenosaunee address to the western world, 1977

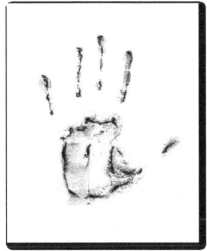

Inuit Story of the Northern Lights

(An Eskimo Legend)

Auroras - or Northern Lights - are believed to be the torches held in the hands of Spirits seeking the souls of those who have just died, to lead them over the abyss terminating the edge of the world. A narrow pathway leads across it to the land of brightness and plenty, where disease and pain are no more, and where food of all kinds is already in abundance. To this place none but the dead and the Raven can go. When the Spirits wish to communicate with the people of the Earth, they make a whistling noise, and the Earth people answer only in a whispering tone. The Eskimo say that they are able to call the Aurora and converse with it. They send messages to the dead through these Spirits.

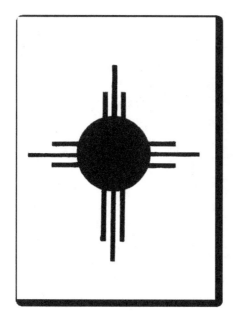

How Old Man Above Created the World

(A Shasta Legend)

Long, long ago, when the world was so new that even the stars were dark, it was very, very flat. Chareya, Old Man Above, could not see through the dark to the new, flat Earth. Neither could he step down to it because it was so far below him. With a large stone he bored a hole in the sky. Then through the hole he pushed down masses of ice and snow, until a great pyramid rose from the plain. Old Man Above climbed down through the hole he had made in the sky, stepping from cloud to cloud, until he could put his foot on top the mass of ice and snow. Then with one long step he reached the Earth.

The sun shone through the hole in the sky and began to melt the ice and snow. It made holes in the ice and snow. When it was soft, Chareya bored with his finger into the earth, here and there, and planted the first trees. Streams from the melting snow watered the new trees and made them grow. Then he gathered the leaves which fell from the trees and blew upon them. They became birds. He took a stick and broke it into pieces. Out of the small end he made fishes and placed them in the mountain streams. Of the middle of the stick, he made all the animals except the grizzly bear. From the big end of the stick came the grizzly bear, who was made master of all. Grizzly was large and strong and cunning. When the Earth was new he walked upon two feet and carried a large club. So strong was Grizzly that Old Man Above feared the creature he had made. Therefore, so that he might be safe, Chareya hollowed out the pyramid of ice and snow as a teepee. There he lived for thousands of snows. The Indians knew he lived there because they could see the smoke curling from the smoke hole of his teepee. When the pale-face came, Old Man Above went away. There is no longer any smoke from the smoke hole. White men call the teepee Mount Shasta.

The Legend of the Cherokee Rose

(Cherokee Legend)

In the latter half of 1838, Cherokee People who had not voluntarily moved west earlier were forced to leave their homes in the East.

The trail to the West was long and treacherous and many were dying along the way. The People's hearts were heavy with sadness and their tears mingled with the dust of the trail.

The Elders knew that the survival of the children depended upon the strength of the women. One evening around the campfire, the Elders called upon Heaven Dweller, *ga lv la di e hi*. They told Him of the People's suffering and tears. They were afraid the children would not survive to rebuild the Cherokee Nation.

Gal v la di e hi spoke to them, "To let you know how much I care, I will give you a sign. In the morning, tell the women to look back along the trail. Where their tears have fallen, I will cause to grow a plant that will have seven leaves for the seven clans of the Cherokee. Amidst the plant will be a delicate white rose with five petals. In the center of the blossom will be a pile of gold to remind the Cherokee of the white man's greed for the gold found on the Cherokee homeland. This plant will be sturdy and strong with stickers on all the stems. It will defy anything which tries to destroy it."

The next morning the Elders told the women to look back down the trail. A plant was growing fast and covering the trail where they had walked. As the women watched, blossoms formed and slowly opened. They forgot their sadness. Like the plant the women began to feel strong and beautiful. As the plant protected its blossoms, they knew they would have the courage and determination to protect their children who would begin a new Nation in the West.

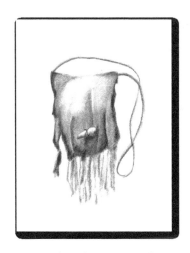

Contents of the Medicine Bag

The contents of each Medicine Bag represent specific totems for specific birth times from around the Medicine Wheel:

The Spirit Rocks and/or animal fetishes represent your own animal totem and your Clan totem

The mineral stone represents your mineral totem

The cloth-wrapped bundle contains your plant totem in seed or herb form

The glass, wooden or stone bead represents your color totem, as does the cloth and ribbon with which your plant totem is wrapped

The empty cloth bundle is to hold some soil from your own most favorite spot on earth

Native Americans, who called themselves "the People," always carried a Medicine Bag or Pouch. Medicine Bags had special power and were good medicine; they were considered sacred. They provided protection, and helped connect with Spirit. The contents of the Medicine Bag were intensely personal, and might include a rock from a sacred place, a special animal tooth, a certain herb, a feather, an animal fetish.

Training began with children who were taught to sit still and enjoy it. They were taught to use their organs of smell, to look where there was apparently nothing to see, and to listen intently when all seemingly was quiet. A child who cannot sit still is a half-developed child.

Luther Standing Bear

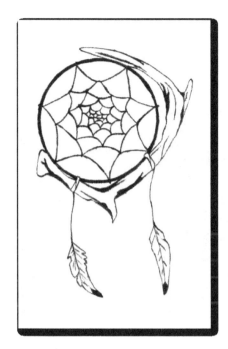

The Legend of the Dream Catcher

The Old Ones tell that dreams hold great power and drift about at night before coming to the sleeping ones.

To keep the dreamer safe, the Old Ones created a special web, the Dream Catcher, to hang above their sleeping places. When dreams traveled the web paths, the bad dreams lost their way and became entangled, disappearing with the first rays of daybreak, like the morning dew on the grass. The good dreams, knowing their way, passed through the center and were guided gently to the sleeping ones.

An old Sioux Indian legend says that dream catchers were hung in lodges and teepees to ensure peaceful dreams. The good dreams, knowing the way, slip through the webbing and slide down the soft feather to the sleeper. The bad dreams, not knowing the way, become entangled in the web, and melt at the first light of the new day. Small dream catchers were hung on cradleboards, so that infants would have only good dreams.

Dreams are not just for the young. They are for children of all ages. To dream is to live, without our dreams we will cease to live and merely exist. Dare to dream and live!

Unknown

Treat the earth well: it was not given to you by your parents, it was loaned to you
by your children. We do not inherit the Earth from our Ancestors; we borrow it from our Children.

Ancient Native American Proverb

The Journey to the Sunrise

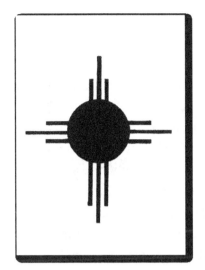

A long time ago several young men made up their minds to find the place where the Sun lives and see what the Sun is like. They got ready their bows and arrows, their parched corn and extra moccasins, and started out toward the east. At first they met tribes they knew, then they came to tribes they had only heard about, and at last to others of which they had never heard.

There was a tribe of root eaters and another of acorn eaters, with great piles of acorn shells near their houses. In one tribe they found a sick man dying, and were told it was the custom there when a man died to bury his wife in the same grave with him. They waited until he was dead, when they saw his friends lower the body into a great pit, so deep and dark that from the top they could not see the bottom. Then a rope was tied around the woman's body, together with a bundle of pine knots, a lighted pine knot was put into her hand, and she was lowered into the pit to die there in the darkness after the last pine knot was burned.

The young men traveled on until they came at last to the sunrise place where the sky reaches down to the ground. They found that the sky was an arch or vault of solid rock hung above the earth and was always swinging up and down, so that when it went up there was an open place like a door between the sky and ground, and when it swung back the door was shut. The Sun came out of this door from the east and climbed along on the inside of the arch. It had a human figure, but was too bright for them to see clearly and too hot to come very near. They waited until the Sun had come out and then tried to get through while the door was still open, but just as the first one was in the doorway the rock came down and crushed him. The other six were afraid to try it, and as they were now at the end of the world they turned around and started back again, but they had traveled so far that they were old men when they reached home.

Once you have heard the meadowlark and caught the scent of fresh-plowed earth, peace cannot escape you.

Sequichie

What the Stars are Like

There are different opinions about the stars. Some say they are balls of light, others say they are human, but most people say they are living creatures covered with luminous fur or feathers.

One night a hunting party camping in the mountains noticed two lights like large stars moving along the top of a distant ridge. They wondered and watched until the light disappeared on the other side. The next night, and the next, they saw the lights again moving along the ridge, and after talking over the matter decided to go on the morrow and try to learn the cause. In the morning they started out and went until they came to the ridge, where, after searching some time, they found two strange creatures about *so* large (making a circle with outstretched arms), with round bodies covered with fine fur or downy feathers, from which small heads stuck out like the heads of terrapins. As the breeze played upon these feathers showers of sparks flew out.

The hunters carried the strange creatures back to the camp, intending to take them home to the settlements on their return. They kept them several days and noticed that every night they would grow bright and shine like great stars, although by day they were only balls of gray fur, except when the wind stirred and made the sparks fly out. They kept very quiet, and no one thought of their trying to escape, when, on the seventh night, they suddenly rose from the ground like balls of fire and were soon above the tops of the trees. Higher and higher they went, while the wondering hunters watched, until at last they were only two bright points of light in the dark sky, and then the hunters knew that they were stars.

What is life? It is the flash of a firefly in the night. It is the breath of a buffalo in the wintertime. It is the little shadow which runs across the grass and loses itself in the sunset.

Crowfoot

How the Terrapin Beat the Rabbit

The Rabbit was a great runner, and everybody knew it. No one thought the Terrapin anything but a slow traveler, but he was a great warrior and very boastful, and the two were always disputing about their speed. At last they agreed to decide the matter by a race. They fixed the day and the starting place and arranged to run across four mountain ridges, and the one who came in first at the end was to be the winner.

The Rabbit felt so sure of it that he said to the Terrapin, "You know you can't run. You can never win the race, so I'll give you the first ridge and then you'll have only three to cross while I go over four."

The Terrapin said that would be all right, but that night when he went home to his family he sent for his Terrapin friends and told them he wanted their help. He said he knew he could not outrun the Rabbit, but he wanted to stop the Rabbit's boasting. He explained his plan to his friends and they agreed to help him.

When the day came all the animals were there to see the race. The Rabbit was with them, but the Terrapin was gone ahead toward the first ridge, as they had arranged, and they could hardly see him on account of the long grass. The word was given and the Rabbit started off with long jumps up the mountain, expecting to win the race before the Terrapin could get down the other side. But before he got up the mountain he saw the Terrapin go over the ridge ahead of him. He ran on, and when he reached the top he looked all around, but could not see the Terrapin on account of the long grass. He kept on down the mountain and began to climb the second ridge, but when he looked up again there was the Terrapin just going over the top. Now he was surprised and made his longest jumps to catch up, but when he got to the top there was the Terrapin away in front going over the third ridge. The Rabbit was getting tired now and nearly out of breath, but he kept on down the mountain and up the other ridge until he got to the top just in time to see the Terrapin cross the fourth ridge and thus win the race.

The Rabbit could not make another jump, but fell over on the ground, crying *mï, mï, mï, mï,* as the Rabbit does ever since when he is too tired to run any more. The race was given to the Terrapin and all the animals wondered how he could win against the Rabbit, but he kept still and never told. It was easy enough, however, because all the Terrapin's friends looked just alike, and he had simply posted one near the top of each ridge to wait until the Rabbit came in sight and then climb over and hide in the long grass. When the Rabbit came on he could not find the Terrapin and so thought the Terrapin was ahead, and if he had met one of the other terrapins he would have thought it the same one because they looked so much alike. The real Terrapin had posted himself on the fourth ridge, so as to

come in at the end of the race and be ready to answer
questions if the animals suspected anything.

Once I was in Victoria, and I saw a very large house. They
told me it was a bank and that the white men place their
money there to be taken care of, and that by and by they got
it back with interest. We are Indians and we have no such
bank; but when we have plenty of money or blankets, we
give them away to other chiefs and people, and by and by
they return them with interest, and our hearts feel good.
Our way of giving is our bank.

Chief Maquinna

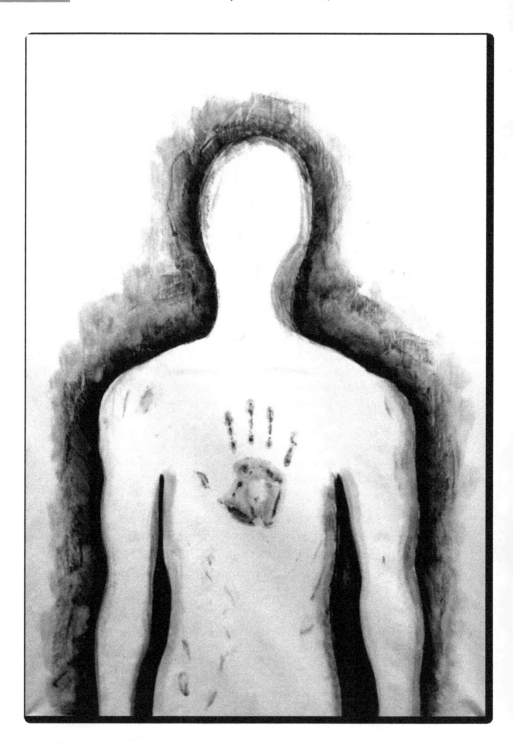

How the Deer got his Horns

In the beginning the Deer had no horns, but his head was smooth just like a doe's. He was a great runner and the Rabbit was a great jumper, and the animals were all curious to know which could go farther in the same time. They talked about it a good deal, and at last arranged a match between the two, and made a nice large pair of antlers for a prize to the winner. They were to start together from one side of a thicket and go through it, then turn and come back, and the one who came out first was to get the horns.

On the day fixed all the animals were there, with the antlers put down on the ground at the edge of the thicket to mark the starting point. While everybody was admiring the horns the Rabbit said: "I don't know this part of the country; I want to take a look through the bushes where I am to run." They thought that all right, so the Rabbit went into the thicket, but he was gone so long that at last the animals suspected he must be up to one of his tricks. They sent a messenger to look for him, and away in the middle of the thicket he found the Rabbit gnawing down the bushes and pulling them away until he had a road cleared nearly to the other side.

The messenger turned around quietly and came back and told the other animals. When the Rabbit came out at last they accused him of cheating, but he denied it until they went into the thicket and found the cleared road. They agreed that such a trickster had no right to enter the race at all, so they gave the horns to the Deer, who was admitted to be the best runner, and he has worn them ever since. They told the Rabbit that as he was so fond of cutting down bushes he might do that for a living hereafter, and so he does to this day.

We must protect the forests for our children, grandchildren and children yet to be born. We must protect the forests for those who can't speak for themselves such as the birds, animals, fish and trees.

Qwatsinas

Why the Turkey Gobbles

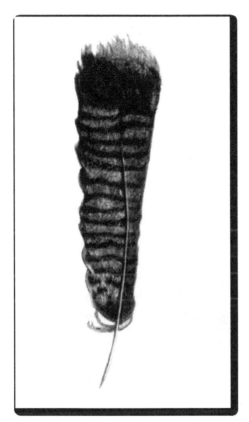

The Grouse used to have a fine voice and a good halloo in the ballplay. All the animals and birds used to play ball in those days and were just as proud of a loud halloo as the ball players of to-day. The Turkey had not a good voice, so he asked the Grouse to give him lessons. The Grouse agreed to teach him, but wanted pay for his trouble, and the Turkey promised to give him some feathers to make himself a collar. That is how the Grouse got his collar of turkey feathers. They began the lessons and the Turkey learned very fast until the Grouse thought it was time to try his voice. "Now," said the Grouse, "I'll stand on this hollow log, and when I give the signal by tapping on it, you must halloo as loudly as you can." So he got upon the log ready to tap on it, as a Grouse does, but when he gave the signal the Turkey was so eager and excited that he could not raise his voice for a shout, but only gobbled, and ever since then he gobbles whenever he hears a noise.

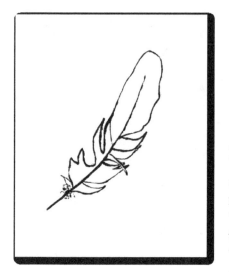

How the Redbird got his Color

A Raccoon passing a Wolf one day made several insulting remarks, until at last the Wolf became angry and turned and chased him. The Raccoon ran his best and managed to reach a tree by the river side before the Wolf came up. He climbed the tree and stretched out on a limb overhanging the water. When the Wolf arrived he saw the reflection in the water, and thinking it was the Raccoon he jumped at it and was nearly drowned before he could scramble out again, all wet and dripping. He lay down on the bank to dry and fell asleep. and while he was sleeping the Raccoon came down the tree and plastered his eves with dung. When the Wolf awoke he found he could not open his eyes, and began to whine. Along came a little brown and through the bushes and beard the Wolf crying and asked what was the matter. The Wolf told his story and said, "If you will get my eyes open, I will show you where to find some nice red paint to paint yourself." "All right," said the brown bird; so he pecked at the Wolf's eyes until he got off all the plaster. Then the Wolf took him to a rock that had streaks of bright red paint running through it, and the little bird painted himself with it, and has ever since been a Redbird.

The Bear Man

(Cherokee Legend)

One springtime morning a Cherokee named Whirlwind told his wife goodbye and left his village to go up in the Smoky Mountains to hunt for wild game. In the forest he saw a black bear and wounded it with an arrow. The bear turned and started to run away, but the hunter followed, shooting one arrow after another into the animal without bringing it down. Whirlwind did not know that this bear possessed secret powers, and could talk and read the thoughts of people.

At last the black bear stopped and pulled the arrows out of his body and gave them to Whirlwind. "It is of no use for you to shoot at me," he said. "You can't kill me. Come with me and I will show you how bears live."

"This bear may kill me," Whirlwind said to himself, but the bear read his thoughts and said, "No, I will not hurt you."

"How can I get anything to eat if I go with this bear," Whirlwind thought, and again the bear knew what the hunter was thinking, and said, "I have plenty of food."

Whirlwind decided to go with the bear. They walked until they came to a cave in the side of a mountain, and the bear said, "This is not where I live, but we are holding a council here and you can see what we do." They entered the cave, which widened as they went farther in until it was as large as a Cherokee long house. It was filled with bears, old and young, brown and black, and one large white bear, who was the chief. Whirlwind sat down in a corner beside the black bear who had brought him inside, but soon the other bears scented his presence.

"What is that bad smell of a man?" one asked, but the bear chief answered, "Don't talk so. It is only a stranger come to see us. Let him alone."

The bears began to talk among themselves, and Whirlwind was astonished that he could understand what they were saying. They were discussing the scarcity of food of all kinds in the mountains, and were trying to decide what to do about it. They had sent messengers in all directions, and two of them had returned to report on what they had found. In a valley to the south, they said, was a large stand of chestnuts and oaks, and the ground beneath them was covered with mast. Pleased at this news, a huge black bear named Long Hams announced he would lead them in a dance.

While they were dancing, the bears noticed Whirlwind's bow and arrows, and Long Hams stopped and said, "This is what men use to kill us. Let us see if we can use them. Maybe we can fight them with their own weapons."

Long Hams took the bow and arrows from Whirlwind. He fitted an arrow and drew back the sinew string, but when he let go, the string caught in his long claws and the arrow fell to the ground. He saw that he could not use the bow and arrows and gave them back to Whirlwind. By this time, the bears had finished their dance, and were leaving the cave to go to their separate homes.

Whirlwind went out with the black bear who had brought him there, and after a long walk they came to a smaller cave in the side of the mountain. "This is where I live," the bear said, and led the way inside. Whirlwind could see no food anywhere in the cave, and wondered how he was going to get something to satisfy his hunger. Reading his thoughts, the bear sat up on his hind legs and made a movement with his forepaws. When he held his paws out to Whirlwind they were filled with chestnuts. He repeated this magic and his paws were filled with huckleberries which he gave to Whirlwind. He then presented him with blackberries, and finally some acorns.

"I cannot eat acorns," Whirlwind said. "Besides, you have given me enough to eat already."

For many moons, through the summer and winter, Whirlwind lived in the cave with the bear. After a while he noticed that his hair was growing all over his body like that of a bear. He learned to eat acorns and act like a bear, but he still walked upright like a man.

On the first warm day of spring the bear told Whirlwind that he had dreamed of the Cherokee village down in the valley. In the dream he heard the Cherokees talking of a big hunt in the mountains.

"Is my wife still waiting there for me?" Whirlwind asked.

"She awaits your return," the bear replied. "But you have become a bear man. If you return you must shut yourself out of sight of your people for seven days without food or drink. At the end of that time you will become like a man again."

A few days later a party of Cherokee hunters came up into the mountains. The black bear and Whirlwind hid themselves in the cave, but the hunters' dogs found the entrance and began to bark furiously.

"I have lost my power against arrows," the bear said. "Your people will kill me and take my skin from me, but they will not harm you. They will take you home with them. Remember what I told you, if you wish to lose your bear nature and become a man again." The Cherokee hunters began throwing lighted pine knots inside the cave.

"They will kill me and drag me outside and cut me in pieces," the bear said. "Afterwards you must cover my blood with leaves. When they are taking you away, if you look back you will see something."

As the bear had foretold, the hunters killed him with arrows and dragged his body outside and took the skin from it and cut the meat into quarters to carry back to their village. Fearing that they might mistake him for another bear, Whirlwind remained in the cave, but the dogs continued barking at him. When the hunters looked inside, they saw a hairy man standing upright, and one of them recognized Whirlwind.

Believing that he had been a prisoner of the bear, they asked him if he would like to go home with them and try to rid himself of his bear nature. Whirlwind replied that he would go with them, but explained that he would have to stay alone in a house for seven days without food or water in order to become as a man again.

While the hunters were loading the meat on their backs, Whirlwind piled leaves over the place where they had killed the bear, carefully covering the drops of blood. After they had walked a short distance down the mountain, Whirlwind looked behind him. He saw a bear rise up out of the leaves, shake himself, and go back into the cave.

When the hunters reached their village, they took Whirlwind to an empty house, and obeying his wishes, barred the entrance door. Although he asked them to say nothing to anyone of his hairiness and his bear nature, one of the hunters must have told of his presence in the village because the very next morning Whirlwind's wife heard that he was there.

She hurried to see the hunters and begged them to let her see her long missing husband.

"You must wait for seven days," the hunters told her. "Come back after seven days, and Whirlwind will return to you as he was when he left the village twelve moons ago."

Bitterly disappointed, the woman went away, but she returned to the hunters each day, pleading with them to let her see her husband. She begged so hard that on the fifth day they took her to the house, unfastened the door, and told Whirlwind to come outside and let his wife see him.

Although he was still hairy and walked like a bear on hind legs, Whirlwind's wife was so pleased to see him again that she insisted he come home with her. Whirlwind went with her, but a few days later he died, and the Cherokees knew that the bears had claimed him because he still had a bear's nature and could not live like a man. If they had kept him shut up in the house without food until the end of the seven days he would have become like a man again. And that is why in that village on the first warm and misty nights of springtime, the ghosts of two bears -- one walking on all fours, the other walking upright -- are still seen to this day.

The Man in the Stump

A man who had a field of growing corn went out one day to see how it was ripening and climbed a tall stump to get a better view. The stump was hollow and a bear had a nest of cubs in the bottom. The man slipped and fell down upon the cubs, which set up such a squealing that the old she-bear heard them and came climbing down into the stump tail first, in bear fashion, to see what was the matter. The  man caught hold of her by the hind legs and the old bear was so frightened that she at once climbed out again, dragging the man, who thus got out of the stump, when the bear ran away.

Take the breath of the new dawn and make it part of you. It will give you strength.

from the Hopi

Determination of Night and Day

(Iroquois)
(IROQUOIS: Smith, *Report of the Bureau of American Ethnology*, ii, 80)

Once upon a time the porcupine was appointed to be the leader of all the animals. Soon after his appointment he called them and presented the question, "Shall we have night and darkness, or daylight with its sunshine?"

This was a very important question, and a violent discussion arose, some wishing for daylight and the sun to rule, and others for continual night.

The chipmunk wished for night and day, weeks and months, and night to be separate from the day, so he began singing, "The light will come; we must have light," which he continued to repeat. Meanwhile the bear began singing, "Night is best; we must have darkness."

While the chipmunk was singing, the day began to dawn. Then the other party saw that the chipmunk was prevailing, and were very angry; and their leader, the bear, pursued the chipmunk, who managed to escape uninjured, the huge paw of the bear simply grazing his back as he entered his hole in a hollow tree, leaving its black imprint, which the chipmunk has ever since retained. But night and day have ever continued to alternate.

The Lost Cherokee

(A Cherokee Legend)

When the first lands were sold by the Cherokee, in 1721, a part of the tribe bitterly opposed the sale, saying that if the Indians once consented to give up any of their territory the whites would never be satisfied, but would soon want a little more, and a little again, until at last there would be none left for the Indians. Finding all they could say not enough to prevent the treaty, they determined to leave their old homes forever and go far into the West, beyond the Great river, where the white men could never follow them. They gave no heed to the entreaties of their friends, but began preparations for the long march, until the others, finding that they could not prevent their going, set to work and did their best to fit them out with pack horses loaded with bread, dried venison, and other supplies.

When all was ready they started, under the direction of their chief. A company of picked men was sent with them to help them in crossing the Great river, and every night until they reached it runners were sent back to the tribe, and out from the tribe to the marching band, to carry messages and keep each party posted as to how the other was getting along. At last they came to the Mississippi, and crossed it by the help of those warriors who had been sent with them. These then returned to the tribe, while the others kept on to the west. All communication was now at all end. No more was heard of the wanderers, and in time the story, of the lost Cherokee was forgotten or remembered only as an old tale.

Still the white man pressed upon the Cherokee and one piece of land after another was sold, until as years went on the dispossessed people began to turn their faces toward the west as their final resting place, and small bands of hunters crossed the Mississippi to learn what might be beyond. One of these parties pushed on across the plains and there at the foot of the great mountains--the Rockies--they found a tribe speaking the old Cherokee language and living still as the Cherokee had lived before they had ever known the white man or his ways.

Hills are always more beautiful than stone buildings. Living in a city is an artificial existence. Lots of people hardly ever feel real soil under their feet, see plants grow except in flower pots, or get far enough beyond the street light to catch the enchantment of a night sky studded with stars. When people live far from scenes of the Great Spirit's making, it's easy for them to forget his laws.

Walking Buffalo

The Legend of the Cedar Tree

(A Cherokee Legend)

A long time ago when the Cherokee people were new upon the earth, they thought that life would be much better if there was never any night. They beseeched the Ouga (Creator) that it might be day all the time and that there would be no darkness.

The Creator heard their voices and made the night cease and it was day all the time. Soon, the forest was thick with heavy growth. It became difficult to walk and to find the path. The people toiled in the gardens many long hours trying to keep the weeds pulled from among the corn and other food plants. It got hot, very hot, and continued that way day after long day. The people began to find it difficult to sleep and became short tempered and argued among themselves.

Not many days had passed before the people realized they had made a mistake and, once again, they beseeched the Creator. "Please," they said, "we have made a mistake in asking that it be day all the time. Now we think that it should be night all the time." The Creator paused at this new request and thought that perhaps the people may be right even though all things were created in twos... representing to us day and night, life and death, good and evil, times of plenty and those times of famine. The Creator loved the people and decided to make it night all the time as they had asked.

The day ceased and night fell upon the earth. Soon, the crops stopped growing and it became very cold. The people spent much of their time gathering wood for the fires. They could not see to hunt meat and with no crops growing it was not long before the people were cold, weak, and very hungry. Many of the people died.

Those that remained still living gathered once again to beseech the Creator. "Help us Creator," they cried! "We have made a terrible mistake. You had made the day and the night perfect, and as it should be, from the beginning. We ask that you forgive us and make the day and night as it was before."

Once again the Creator listened to the request of the people. The day and the night became, as the people had asked, as it had been in the beginning. Each day was divided between light and darkness. The weather became more pleasant, and the crops began to grow again. Game was plentiful and the hunting was good. The people had plenty to eat and there was not much sickness. The people treated each other with compassion and respect. It was good to be alive. The people thanked the Creator for their life and for the food they had to eat.

The Creator accepted the gratitude of the people and was glad to see them smiling again. However, during the time of the long days of night, many of the people had died, and the Creator was sorry that they had perished because of the night. The Creator placed their spirits in a newly created tree. This tree was named *a-tsi-na tlu-gv* {ah-see-na loo-guh} cedar tree.

When you smell the aroma of the cedar tree or gaze upon it standing in the forest, remember that if you are Tsalagi {Cherokee}, you are looking upon your ancestor.

Tradition holds that the wood of the cedar tree holds powerful protective spirits for the Cherokee. Many carry a small piece of cedar wood in their medicine bags worn around the neck. It is also placed above the entrances to the house to protect against the entry of evil spirits. A traditional drum would be made from cedar wood.

It was our belief that the love of possessions is a weakness to be overcome. Its appeal is to the material part, and if allowed its way, it will in time disturb one's spiritual balance. Therefore, children must early learn the beauty of generosity. They are taught to give what they prize most, that they may taste the happiness of giving.

Ohiyesa

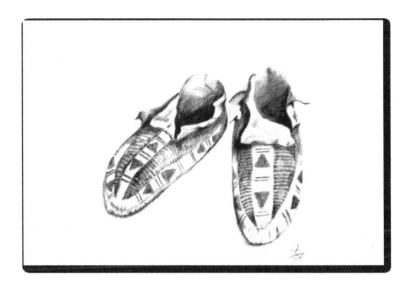

The First Moccisons

There was once a great chief on the Plains who had very tender feet. Other mighty chiefs laughed at him; little chiefs only smiled as he hobbled past; and though they did not dare to smile, the people of the tribe also enjoyed the big chief's discomfort. All of them were in the same canoe, having no horses and only bare feet, but luckily very few of them had tender feet. The unhappy medicine man who was advisor to the Chief-of-the-Tender-Feet was afraid and troubled. Each time he was called before the chief he was asked, 'What are you going to do about it?" The 'it' meant the chief's tender feet.

Forced by fear, the medicine man at last hit upon a plan. Though he knew that it was not the real answer to the chief's foot problem, nevertheless it was a good makeshift. The medicine man had some women of the tribe weave a long, narrow mat of reeds, and when the big chief had to go anywhere, four braves unrolled the mat in front of him so that he walked in comfort. One day, the braves were worn out from seeing that the chief's feet were not worn out. They carelessly unrolled the mat over a place where flint arrowheads had been chipped. The arrowheads had long ago taken flight, but the needle-sharp chips remained. When the big chief's tender feet were wounded by these chips, he uttered a series of whoops which made the nearby aspen tree leaves quiver so hard that they have been trembling ever since.

That night the poor medicine man was given an impossible task by the angry chief: 'Cover the whole earth with mats so thick that my feet will not suffer. If you fail, you will die when the moon is round.'

The frightened maker of magic crept back to his lodge. He did not wish to be put to death on the night of the full moon, but he could think of no way to avoid it. Suddenly he saw the hide of an elk which he had killed pegged to the ground, with two women busily scraping the hair from the hide, and an idea flashed into his groping mind. He sent out many hunters; many women were busy for many days; many braves with hunting knives cut, and women sewed with bone needles and rawhide sinews.

On the day before the moon was round, the medicine man went to the chief and told him that he had covered as much of the earth as was possible in so short a time. When the chief looked from the door of his lodge, he saw many paths of skin stretching as far as he could see. Long strips which could be moved from place to place connected the main leather paths. Even the chief thought that this time the magic of the medicine man had solved tenderfoot transportation for all time - but this was not to be !

One day, as the big chief was walking along one of his smooth, tough leather paths, he saw a pretty maiden of the tribe gliding ahead of him, walking on the hard earth on one side of the chief's pathway. She glanced back when she heard the pitter- patter of his feet on the elk hide pathway and seemed to smile. The chief set off on the run to catch up with her, his eyes fixed on the back of She-Who-Smiled, and so his feet strayed from the narrow path and landed in a bunch of needle-sharp thorns! The girl ran for her life when she heard the hideous howls of the chief, and Indians in the distant village thought that they were being attacked by wildcats.

Two suns later, when the chief was calm enough to speak again, he had his medicine man brought before him and told the unhappy man that next day, when the sun was high, he would be sent with all speed to the land of shadows.

That night, the medicine man climbed to the top of a high hill in search of advice from friendly spirits on how to cover the entire earth with leather. He slept, and in a dream vision he was shown the answer to his problem. Amid vivid flashes of lightning, he tore down the steep hillside, howling louder than the big chief at times, as jagged rocks wounded his bare feet and legs. He did not stop until he was safely inside his lodge. He worked all night and until the warriors who were to send him on the shadow trail came for him, just before noon the next day. He was surrounded by the war-club armed guards. He was clutching close to his heart something tightly rolled in a piece of deerskin. His cheerful smile surprised those who saw him pass. 'Wah, he is brave!' said the men of the tribe. 'He is very brave!' said the women of the tribe.

The big chief was waiting just outside his lodge. He gave the guards swift, stern orders. Before the maker of magic could be led away, he asked leave to say a few words to the chief. 'Speak!' said the chief, sorry to lose a clever medicine man who was very good at most kinds of magic. Even the chief knew that covering the entire earth with leather was an impossible task.

The medicine man quickly knelt beside the chief, unrolled the two objects which he took from his bundle and slipped one of them on each foot of the chief. The chief seemed to be wearing a pair of bear's hairless feet, instead of bare feet, and he was puzzled at first as he looked at the elk hide handicraft of his medicine man. 'Big chief,' the medicine man exclaimed joyfully, 'I have found the way to cover the earth with leather! For you, O chief, from now on the earth will always be covered with leather.' And so it was.

Now tell me this one little thing, if you have any sense. Which of these two is the wisest and happiest--he who labors without ceasing and only obtains, and that with great trouble, enough to live on, or he who rests in comfort and finds all that he needs in the pleasures of hunting and fishing?

Gaspesian Chief

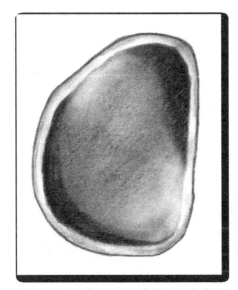

The Legend of the Apache Tear

(An Apache Legend)

In the 1870's, a tribe of Pinal Apache Indians carried out raids against the white farmers and friendly Pima Indians. The Arizona Volunteers followed the Apaches on a secret trail to the top of some rugged, towering cliffs. They attacked at daybreak, killing over half of the 75 Apaches. The remaining Apaches chose death by leaping over the cliff's edge rather than die at the hands of the attackers.

It is said that the sorrow of the Apache women was so great that the Great Father embedded their tears into black stones at the foot of the cliff. These black obsidian stones, when held to the light, reveal the translucent tear.

(Apache tears are actually small pieces of obsidian or volcanic glass. When held in the palm of your hand, the stone appears to be black. When held to the light, you are able to see through the stone.)

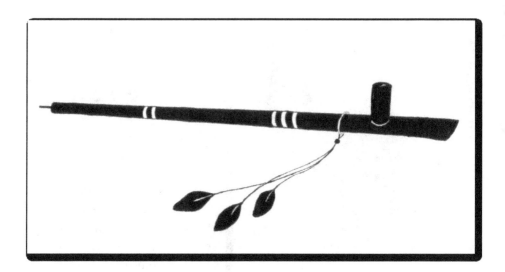

The Gift of the Peace Pipe

One day, two young men were hunting wild game for their village. There were not many large game in the region and the people were hungry. While wading through snowdrifts among the trees, they were startled to see a beautiful young woman standing before them. She was dressed in pretty robes, and in her hand she held a small bundle. The young men could not think of anything to say, so they just stood and looked at her.

"Do not fear," said the woman, "I bring you peace and happiness. Now tell me, why are you so far from your village?"

Her grace and beauty so fired the older brave with love that he could not speak. Finally, the younger man spoke.

"Our village is in need of more food," he said. "We are hunting."

"Here," she said, "take this bundle back to your people. Tell the Chiefs of the seven campfires to meet in the council lodge and wait for me."

The two men still could think of nothing to say. The older brave, blinded by love for the beautiful woman, reached out to touch her. As he did so, she touched him lightly on the head and he fell to the ground. A cloud enveloped his body, and all that was left of him was a pile of white bones. Then, as suddenly as she appeared, she disappeared.

The younger brave realized that his companion had "evil thoughts" about the woman, and that's why he was punished. He then hurried back to the village to tell the Chiefs. The next day the seven Chiefs put on their best feathers and robes and sat in a circle, all looking down at the bundle which had not been opened.

A sudden blow of wind passed. When it had gone the Chiefs saw before them a beautiful woman dressed in pretty robes. None of them could find words in their mouths. So she spoke to them:

"I bring you a message of peace. Your people are great hunters and brave warriors. When the sun rises again, pack your belongings and travel toward the setting sun. There a great land awaits you. You will find beyond the Father of Waters new animals and other tribes of people. In this bundle is a pipe to bring you peace with all the people."

The woman took out a pipe made from bone and decorated with bird feathers. Then she left the lodge and disappeared.

Soon the tribes moved westward. They came to the Mississippi River which was called the Father of Waters, and then to the Missouri River and the Black Hills. They saw for the first time the animals we call horses, and there were great herds of buffalo.

To make peace with the other tribes, the Sioux chieftains brought out their peace pipe. The pipe was usually handed to the Chief of the enemy tribe first and then it was smoked by all the leaders of both tribes. Later, when the white men came to the Sioux country, the Indians brought out their pipe of peace to smoke, but the white men would not smoke it.

A great amount of soft red stone was found for making pipes and every year all the Sioux tribes would send some of their people to the pipestone quarries to smoke the pipe of peace with other tribes. This place came to be known as Pipestone, the name which it carries to this day as a town and Indian school in Minnesota.

A Sioux once said, "the pipe is us. the stem is our backbone, the bowl our head, the stone our blood, red as our skin."

Pipes are among the most sacred objects to the Lakota being used in ceremonies. the more decorated the pipe -- the stronger its powers.

Brother of the Moon

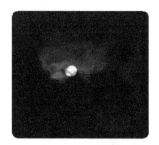

(Cherokee)

As the Cherokee's conception of Christ did not fit any European style Christmas ceremony and the fact that we, the Tsa la gi have been upon this earth a long, long time, we had our own ways of celebrating and giving thanks. Since back then, the ways have changed, however some things stay the same. The seasons don't change, the significance of 4 stays the same and that of 7 also does not change. It can be said that the celebrations were held this way or that but we were not there and these are closely guarded secrets. Perhaps they will be shared when the time is right perhaps, if we were there at a celebration of long ago at this time of the changing of seasons it would have gone something like this:

It is the time of change when the leaves are red and upon the earth and the bare branches of the trees sigh a bit of relief to shed their burden. The winter coats are thick and warm on the creatures of our mother Our brother the Bear is in the womb of earth mother contemplating the coming seasons and dreaming of ripe berries. The old man of the North has blanketed the earth mother with a fresh coat of snow and the promise of regeneration lies just below it. It is the time of the changing of seasons from the time of harvesting to winter and the time to give thanks for the year we have had and the year to come.

As the spirit world is the most powerful at dawn or sunrise the ceremony will be at sunrise. The villagers gather at the sacred fire pit and the keeper of the sacred fire adds the ashes from the previous fire to this and the fire glows. This insures the circle continues from one fire to the next, from one season to the other from one generation to the next.

A man of medicine leads us in our prayers, song and thanks. He speaks his silent prayer asking the spirits of the 4 directions to help him carry the prayers to the creator. He asks the sun father and star nation of the skies to also help carry the prayers of thanks. He asks the mother of us all to give her blessing and help carry the prayers and for the Tsa la gi, the 7th spirit. Sometimes called in different ways it is the power within us, the power around us it is that of our beings our own spirit, it is also asked to help carry our prayers and bless us this day.

As the sun rises and we stand facing the east we sing. We sing a song of welcome to the sun and we pray. It is time to thank the creator for the food stores that will get us thru the winter and to thank the creatures of the earth for giving their lives so that we and our families may live. It is time to thank the earth mother for being good to us and for the plant people she provides us that heal and nourish us.

We pray around the fire and give thanks for all these things and we pray for the coming year and that it may be good to the earth mother. For if it is good to her, it will be good for us and the creatures of the earth. We also at this time thank the Corn Mothers for providing us with her corn, which is a large part of our daily nourishment. We share grits passed to show that we are grateful and to forgive the things of the past. We will sing and pray and perhaps dance this day, as we are grateful to the spirits and show our love for the earth and one another. It is another passing of the seasons.

One more way we give thanks near this day called Christmas.

Dream Walk

(*A Lakota Legend*)

Long ago when the world was young, an old Lakota spiritual leader was on a high mountain and had a vision. In his vision, Iktomi, the great trickster and searcher of wisdom, appeared in the form of a spider. Iktomi spoke to him in a sacred language. As he spoke, Iktomi the spider picked up the elder's willow hoop which had feathers, horsehair, beads and offerings on it, and began to spin a web. He spoke to the elder about the cycles of life, how we begin our lives as infants, move on through childhood and on to adulthood. Finally we go to old age where we must be taken care of as infants, completing the cycle.

"But", Iktomi said as he continued to spin his web, "in each time of life there are many forces, some good and some bad. If you listen to the good forces, they will steer you in the right direction. But, if you listen to the bad forces, they'll steer you in the wrong direction and may hurt you. So these forces can help, or can interfere with the harmony of Nature. While the spider spoke, he continued to weave his web.

When Iktomi finished speaking, he gave the elder the web and said, "The web is a perfect circle with a hole in the center. Use the web to help your people reach their goals, making good use of their ideas, dreams and visions. If you believe in the great spirit, the web will catch your good ideas and the bad ones will go through the hole."

The elder passed on his vision onto the people and now many Indian people have a dream catcher above their bed to sift their dreams and visions. The good is captured in the web of life and carried with the people, but the evil in their dreams drops through the hole in the web and are no longer a part of their lives. It is said the dream catcher holds the destiny of the future.

When you arise in the morning, give thanks for the morning light, for your life and strength. Give thanks for your food and the joy of living. If you see no reason for giving thanks, the fault lies in yourself.

Tecumseh

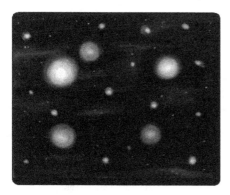

How The Milky Way Came To Be

(A Cherokee Legend)

Long ago when the world was young, there were not many stars in the sky.

In those days the people depended on corn for their food. Dried corn could be made into corn meal by placing it inside a large hollowed stump and pounding it with a long wooden pestle. The cornmeal was stored in large baskets. During the winter, the ground meal could made into bread and mush.

One morning an old man and his wife went to their storage basket for some cornmeal. They discovered that someone or something had gotten into the cornmeal during the night. This upset them very much for no one in a Cherokee village stole from someone else.

Then they noticed that the cornmeal was scattered over the ground. In the middle of the spilt meal were giant dog prints. These dog prints were so large that the elderly couple knew this was no ordinary dog.

They immediately alerted the people of the village. It was decided that this must be a spirit dog from another world. The people did not want the spirit dog coming to their village. They decided to get rid of the dog by frightening it so bad it would never return. They gathered their drums and turtle shell rattles and later that night they hid around the area where the cornmeal was kept.

Late into the night they heard a whirring sound like many bird wings. They look up to see the form of a giant dog swooping down from the sky. It landed near the basket and then began to eat great mouthfuls of cornmeal.

Suddenly the people jumped up beating and shaking their noise makers. The noise was so loud it sounded like thunder. The giant dog turned and began to run down the path. The people chased after him making the loudest noises they could. It ran to the top of a hill and leaped into the sky, the cornmeal spilling out the sides of its mouth.

The giant dog ran across the black night sky until it disappeared from sight. But the cornmeal that had spilled from its mouth made a path way across the sky. Each gain of cornmeal became a star.

The Cherokees call that pattern of stars, gi li' ut sun stan un' yi (gil-LEE-oot-soon stan-UNH-yee), "the place where the dog ran."

And that is how the Milky Way came to be.

The Star Feathers

A long time ago a warrior of roving disposition went down into the white settlements toward the east, where for the first time he saw a peacock. The beautiful long feathers surprised and delighted him, and by trading some valuable Indian possession of his own he managed to buy a few of them, which he took with him to the mountains and hid, until he was ready to use them, in an old beaver lodge under the river bank. To get into the beaver lodge he had to dive under the water.

Then he set to work secretly and made himself a headdress, with the long peacock feathers in the front and trailing out behind and the shorter ones at the sides. At the next dance he wore the new headdress, and asserted that he had been up to the sky and that these were star feathers. He made a long speech also, which he pretended was a message he had received from the star spirits to deliver to the people.

Everyone wondered at the beautiful feathers, so different from any they had ever seen before. They made no doubt that he had been up to the sky and talked with spirits. He became a great prophet, and used to keep himself hidden all day in the beaver hole, and whenever there was a night gathering for a dance or a council he would suddenly appear among them wearing his feather headdress and give the people a new message from the sky. Then he would leave them again, pretending that he went up to heaven.

He grew famous, and powerful among all the medicine men, until at last it happened that another Cherokee went down among the white settlements and saw there another peacock, and knew at once that the prophet was a fraud. On his return he quietly told some of his friends, and they decided to investigate. When the next night dance came around the prophet was on hand as usual with a new message fresh from the stars. The people listened reverently, and promised to do all that he commanded. Then he left them, saying that he must return at once to the sky, but as he went out from the circle the spies followed him in the darkness, and saw him go down to the river and dive under the water. They waited, but he, did not come up again, and they went back and told the people. The next morning a party went to the spot and discovered the beaver lodge under the bank. One man dived and came up inside, and there he found the prophet sitting with the peacock feathers by his side.

A long time ago, the Creator came to Turtle Island and said to the Red People, "You will be the keepers of the Mother Earth. Among you I will give the wisdom about Nature, about the interconnectedness of all things, about balance, and about living in harmony. You Red People will see the secrets of Nature. You will live in hardship and the blessing of this is you will stay close to the Creator. The day will come when you will need to share the secrets with other people of the earth because they will stray from their Spiritual ways. The time to start sharing is today.

Don Coyhis

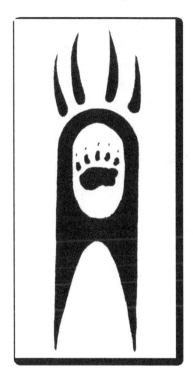

The Ballgame Between the Birds and the Animals

The old ones tell us that one time, the animals challenged the birds to a great ballgame, and the birds accepted. The leaders of each group made the plans and set the date, and when the time came, both parties met at the place for the ball dance. The animals met on a nice smooth grassy area near the river, and the birds perched in the treetops overlooking the animals. The captain of the animal team was Yona, the bear, and he was strong and heavy, and could take care of anyone who got in his way. All along the way to the ballgame, he was showing his strength by tossing logs and boulders into the air. He boasted of what he would do to the birds at the ballgame. Dagasi, the terrapin, was a huge terrapin, and his shell was so hard, not even the heaviest blow to him would hurt. He kept standing on his hind legs and then dropping to the ground, bragging that this is what he would do at the ballgame. He would crush any bird that tried to take the ball from him. There was also Awi, the deer, who could easily outrun any and every animal. They thought they had a great team.

The birds had Wohali, the eagle, as their captain. Tawodi, the hawk, and other strong birds were on their side.

Although they were swift and strong, they were still a little afraid of the animals. After the dance, they were all pruning their feathers while perched in the trees, and waited for the captain to give the word. All of a sudden, here came two little things hardly bigger than field mice, and they climbed up the tree where Wohali, the bird captain, was sitting. They asked to join in the game. The captain looked at them, and seeing that they were four-legged, asked why they didn't go down to the animal team. They said they had, but the animals laughed at them, and made fun of them, because they were so small. Wohali felt sorry for them, and wanted to take them.

But they had no wings. Wohali, Tawodi, and the others consulted, and finally decided to make some wings for the little ones. They tried for a very long time to think of a solution, when finally someone thought about the drum they had used in the dance. The head was made of groundhog skin, and maybe they could take off a corner of it and make some wings. They took two pieces from the drum head and cut them into shape for wings, and stretched them with cane splints and fastened them to the front legs of one of the little animals.

This is how Tlameha, the bat, came to be.

They threw the ball to him and told him to catch it. He dodged and circled about, and always kept the ball in the air and never let it hit the ground. The birds soon felt that he would be one of their best players.

Now they figured they better fix the other poor animal, but they had no more leather to make wings. Somebody thought of stretching his skin, the way the leather had been stretched on the drum. Two large birds took hold from each side of him with their strong beaks, and pulled at his fur for several minutes. They managed to stretch the skin between his front and back legs, until they had Tewa, the flying squirrel. To see how well he could play, the captain threw the ball up in the air, and Tewa leaped off the limb, caught it in his teeth, and carried it through the air until he reached another tree, far, far away.

When everyone was ready, the signal was given and the game began. Almost at the very first, Tewa caught the ball and carried it to a tree, from which he threw it to the other birds. They kept it in the air for a very long time, but it finally dropped. Yona rushed to grab it, but Tlutlu, the martin, darted after it and threw it to Tlameha, the bat. By his dodging and circling, he kept it out of the way of even Awi, the deer, until finally Tlameha threw it to the pole and won the game for the birds.

Yona and Dagasi, who had bragged about how good they were and what they would do to the birds, never even got a chance to play. For saving the ball when it dropped, they gave Tlutlu, the martin, a beautiful gourd in which he could build his nest. Today, he still has it.

Ghost Stallion

(A Yinnuwok Legend)

This is a tale the old men tell around the fire, when the stars are blown clean on a windy night, and the coyotes are howling on the Cree Jump. And when, sometimes, over the wind, comes clearly the sound of running horses, their

hearers move a little closer to one another and pile more wood on the fire.

This is a story from a long time ago, say the Old Ones. What the man's name was, no one knows now, and so they call him "The Traveler".

Long ago, The Traveler was a wealthy chief. A warrior in his young days, he had taken many scalps, many horses, and many another trophy of value. And he had increased his possessions by hard dealings with that less fortunate, and by gambling with younger men who were no match for his cunning.

His fellow tribesmen did not love him although they admired his bravery, for in times of hardship, when other chiefs shared freely whatever they had, he drove hard bargains and generally prospered from the ills of others. His wives he had abused till their parents took them away; his children hated him, and he had no love for them.

There was only one thing he cared for: his horses. They were fine horses, beautiful horses, for he kept only the best; and when a young warrior returned from a raid with a particularly good horse, The Traveler never rested until (whether by fair means or not) he had it in his possession. At night, when the dance drum was brought out, and the other Indians gathered round it, The Traveler went alone to the place where his horses were picketed, to gloat over his treasures. He loved them. But he loved only the ones that were young, and handsome, and healthy a horse that was old, or sick, or injured, received only abuse.

One morning, when he went to the little valley in which his horses were kept, he found in the herd an ugly white stallion. He was old, with crooked legs, and a matted coat, thin, and tired looking.

The Traveler flew into a rage. He took his rawhide rope, and caught the poor old horse. Then, with a club, he beat him unmercifully. When the animal fell to the ground, stunned, The Traveler broke his legs with the club, and left him to die. He returned to his lodge, feeling not the slightest remorse for his cruelty.

Later, deciding he might as well have the hide of the old horse, he returned to the place where he had left him. But, to his surprise, the white stallion was gone. That night, as The Traveler slept, he had a dream. The white stallion appeared to him, and slowly turned into a beautiful horse, shining white, with long mane and tail - a horse more lovely than any The Traveler had ever seen.

Then the Stallion spoke: "If you had treated me kindly," the stallion said, "I would have brought you more horses. You were cruel to me, so I shall take away the horses you have!"

When The Traveler awoke, he found his horses were gone. All that day, he walked and searched, but when at nightfall he fell asleep exhausted, he had found no trace of them. In his dreams, the White Stallion came again, and said, "Do you wish to find your horses? They are north, by a lake. You will sleep twice, before you come to it."

As soon as he awakened in the morning, The Traveler hastened northward. Two days' journey, and when he came to the lake there were no horses. That night, the Ghost Stallion came again. "Do you wish to find your horses?" he said. "They are east, in some hills. There will be two sleeps before you came to the place.'

When the sun had gone down on the third day, The Traveler had searched the hills, but had found no horses. And so it went night after night the Stallion came to The Traveler, directing him to some distant spot, but he never found his horses. He grew thin, and his feet were sore. Sometimes he got a horse from some friendly camp; sometimes he stole one, in the night. But always, before morning, would come a loud drumming of hoofs, the Ghost Stallion and his band would gallop by, and the horse of The Traveler would break its picket, and go with them.

And never again did he have a horse; never again did he see his own lodge. And he wanders, even to this day, the old men say, still searching for his lost horses.

Sometimes, they say, on a windy autumn night when the stars shine very clearly, and over on the Cree Jump the coyote's howl, above the wind you may hear a rush of running horses, and the stumbling footsteps of an old man. And, if you are very unlucky, you may see the Stallion and his band, and The Traveler, still pursuing them, still trying to get back his beautiful horses.

When you arise in the morning, give thanks for the morning light, for your life and strength. Give thanks for your food and the joy of living. If you see no reason for giving thanks, the fault lies in yourself.

Tecumseh

Ataga'hi, The Enchanted Lake

A Cherokee Legend)

Westward from the headwaters of Oconaluftee river, in the wildest depths of the Great Smoky mountains, which form the line between North Carolina and Tennessee, is the enchanted lake of Ataga'hi. (Gall place)

Although all the Cherokee know that it is there, no one has ever seen it, for the way is so difficult that only the animals know how to reach it. Should a stray hunter come near the place he would know of it by the whirring sound of the thousands of wild ducks flying about the lake.

On reaching the spot he would find only a dry flat, without bird or animal or blade of grass, unless he had first sharpened his spiritual vision by prayer and fasting and an all-night vigil.

Because it is not seen, some people think the lake has dried up long ago, but this is not true. To one who had kept watch and fast through the night it would appear at daybreak as a wide-extending but shallow sheet of purple water, fed by springs spouting from the high cliffs around.

In the water are all kinds of fish and reptiles, and swimming upon the surface or flying overhead are great flocks of ducks and pigeons, while all about the shores are bear tracks crossing in every direction. It is the medicine lake of the birds and animals, and whenever a bear is wounded by the hunters he makes his way through the woods to this lake and plunges into the water, and when he comes out upon the other side his wounds are healed.

For this reason the animals keep the lake invisible to the hunter.

Chipmunk and Bear

(An Iroquois Legend)

Long ago when animals could talk, a bear was walking along. Now it has always been said that bears think very highly of themselves. Since they are big and strong, they are certain that they are the most important of the animals.

As this bear went along turning over big logs with his paws to look for food to eat, he felt very sure of himself. "There is nothing I cannot do," said this bear.

 "Is that so?" said a small voice. Bear looked down. There was a little chipmunk looking up at Bear from its hole in the ground.

"Yes," Bear said, "that is true indeed." He reached out one huge paw and rolled over a big log. "Look at how easily I can do this. I am the strongest of all the animals. I can do anything. All the other animals fear me."

"Can you stop the sun from rising in the morning?" said the Chipmunk.

Bear thought for a moment. "I have never tried that," he said. "Yes, I am sure I could stop the sun from rising."

"You are sure?" said Chipmunk.

"I am sure," said Bear. "Tomorrow morning the sun will not rise. I, Bear, have said so." Bear sat down facing the east to wait.

Behind him the sun set for the night and still he sat there. The chipmunk went into its hole and curled up in its snug little nest, chuckling about how foolish Bear was. All through the night Bear sat. Finally the first birds started their songs and the east glowed with the light which comes before the sun.

"The sun will not rise today," said Bear. He stared hard at the glowing light. "The sun will not rise today."

However, the sun rose, just as it always had. Bear was very upset, but Chipmunk was delighted. He laughed and laughed. "Sun is stronger than Bear," said the chipmunk, twittering with laughter. Chipmunk was so amused that he came out of his hole and began running around in circles, singing this song:

"The sun came up,
The sun came up.
Bear is angry,
But the sun came up."

While Bear sat there looking very unhappy, Chipmunk ran around and around, singing and laughing until he was so weak that he rolled over on his back. Then, quicker than the leap of a fish from a stream, Bear shot out one big paw and pinned him to the ground.

"Perhaps I cannot stop the sun from rising," said Bear, "but you will never see another sunrise."

'Oh, Bear," said the chipmunk. "oh, oh, oh, you are the strongest, you are the quickest, you are the best of all of the animals. I was only joking." But Bear did not move his paw.

"Oh, Bear," Chipmunk said, "you are right to kill me, I deserve to die. Just please let me say one last prayer to Creator before you eat me."

"Say your prayer quickly," said Bear. "Your time to walk the Sky Road has come!"

"Oh, Bear," said Chipmunk, "I would like to die. But you are pressing down on me so hard I cannot breathe. I can hardly squeak. I do not have enough breath to say a prayer. If you would just lift your paw a little, just a little bit, then I could breathe. And I could say my last prayer to the Maker of all, to the one who made great, wise, powerful Bear and the foolish, weak, little Chipmunk.

"Bear lifted up his paw. He lifted it just a little bit. That little bit, though, was enough. Chipmunk squirmed free and ran for his hole as quickly as the blinking of an eye. Bear swung his paw at the little chipmunk as it darted away. He was not quick enough to catch him, but the very tips of his long claws scraped along Chipmunk's back leaving three pale scars.

To this day, all chipmunks wear those scars as a reminder to them of what happens when one animal makes fun to another.

Gluscabi and the Wind Eagle

(An Abenaki Legend)

Long ago, Gluscabi lived with his grandmother,
Woodchuck, in a small lodge beside the big water.

One day Gluscabi was walking around when he looked out
and saw some ducks in the bay.

"I think it is time to go hunt some ducks," he said. So he
took his bow and arrows and got into his canoe. He began
to paddle out into the bay and as he paddled he sang:

Ki yo wah ji neh
yo hey ho hey
Ki yo wah ji neh
Ki yo wah ji neh

But a wind came up and it turned his canoe and blew him back to shore. Once again Gluscabi began to paddle out and this time he sang his song a little harder.

KI YO WAH JI NEH
YO HEY HO HEY
KI YO WAH JI NEH
KI YO WAH JI NEH

But again the wind came and blew him back to shore. Four times he tried to paddle out into the bay and four times he failed.

He was not happy. He went back to the lodge of his grandmother and walked right in, even though there was a stick leaning across the door, which meant that the person inside was doing some work and did not want to be disturbed.

"Grandmother," Gluscabi asked, "What makes the wind blow?"

Grandmother Woodchuck looked up from her work. "Gluscabi," she said, "Why do you want to know?"

Then Gluscabi answered her just as every child in the world does when they are asked such a question. "Because," he said.

Grandmother Woodchuck looked at him. "Ah, Gluscabi, " she said. "Whenever you ask such questions I feel there is going to be trouble. And perhaps I should not tell you. But I know that you are very stubborn and would never stop asking. So, I shall tell you. If you walk always facing the wind you will come to the place where Wuchowsen stands."

"Thank you, Grandmother," said Gluscabi. He stepped out of the lodge and faced into the wind and began to walk.

He walked across the fields and through the woods and the wind blew hard. He walked through the valleys and into the hills and the wind blew harder still. He came to the foothills and began to climb and the wind still blew harder.

Now the foothills were becoming mountains and the wind was very strong. Soon there were no longer any trees and the wind was very, very strong.

The wind was so strong that it blew off Gluscabi's moccasins. But he was very stubborn and he kept on walking, leaning into the wind. Now the wind was so strong that it blew off his shirt, but he kept on walking. Now the wind was so strong that it blew off all his clothes and he was naked, but he still kept walking.

Now the wind was so strong that it blew off his hair, but Gluscabi still kept walking, facing into the wind. The wind was so strong that it blew off his eyebrows, but he still continued to walk.

Now the wind was so strong that he could hardly stand. He had to pull himself along by grabbing hold of the boulders. But there, on the peak ahead of him, he could see a great bird flapping its wings. It was Wuchowsen, the Wind Eagle.

Gluscabi took a deep breath, "GRANDFATHER!" he shouted.

The Wind Eagle stopped flapping his wings and looked around. "Who calls me Grandfather?" he said.

Gluscabi stood up. "It's me, Grandfather. I came up here to tell you that you do a very good job making the wind blow."

The Wind Eagle puffed out his chest with pride. "You mean like this?" he said and flapped his wings even harder. The wind that he made was so strong that it lifted Gluscabi right off his feet, and he would have been blown right off the mountain had he not reached out and grabbed a boulder again.

"GRANDFATHER!!!" Gluscabi shouted again.

The Wind Eagle stopped flapping his wings. "Yes?" he said.

Gluscabi stood up and came closer to Wuchowsen. "You do a very good job of making the wind blow, Grandfather. This is so. But it seems to me that you could do an even better job if you were on that peak over there."

The Wind Eagle looked over toward the other peak. "That may be so," he said, "but how would I get from here to there?"

Gluscabi smiled. "Grandfather," he said, "I will carry you. Wait here."

Then Gluscabi ran back down the mountain until he came to a big basswood tree. He stripped off the outer bark and from the inner bark he braided a strong carrying strap which he took back up the mountain to the Wind Eagle.

"Here, Grandfather," he said, "let me wrap this around you so I can lift you more easily." Then he wrapped the carrying strap so tightly around Wuchowsen that his wings were pulled in to his sides and he could hardly breathe.

"Now, Grandfather," said Gluscabi, picking the Wind Eagle up, "I will take you to a better place."

He began to walk toward the other peak, but as he walked he came to a place where there was a large crevice, and as he stepped over it he let go of the carrying strap and the Wind Eagle slid down into the crevice, upside down, and was stuck.

"Now," Gluscabi said, "it is time to go hunt some ducks."

He walked back down the mountain and there was no wind at all. He waited till he came to the tree line and still no wind blew. He walked down to the foothills and down to the hills and the valleys and still there was no wind. He walked through the forest and the fields and the wind did not blow at all.

He walked and walked until he got back to the lodge by the water, and by now all his hair had grown back.

He put on some fine new clothing and a new pair of moccasins and took his bow and arrows and went back to the bay and climbed into his boat to hunt ducks.

He paddled out into the water and sang his canoeing song:

Ki yo wah ji neh
yo hey ho hey
Ki yo wah ji neh
Ki yo wah ji neh

But the air was very hot and still and he began to sweat.
The air was so still and hot that it was hard to breathe. Soon
the water began to grow dirty and smell bad and there was
so much foam on the water he could hardly paddle.

He was not pleased at all and he returned to the shore and
went straight to his grandmother's lodge and walked in.

"Grandmother," he said, "what is wrong? The air is hot and
still and it is making me sweat and it is hard to breathe. The
water is dirty and covered with foam. I cannot hunt ducks
at all like this."

Grandmother Woodchuck looked up at Gluscabi.
"Gluscabi," she said, "what have you done now?"

And Gluscabi answered just as every child in the world
answers when asked that question, "Oh, nothing," he said.

"Gluscabi," said Grandmother Woodchuck again, "Tell me
what you have done."

Then Gluscabi told her about going to visit the Wind Eagle
and what he had done to stop the wind.

"Oh, Gluscabi," said Grandmother Woodchuck, "will you
never learn? Tabaldak, The Owner, set the Wind Eagle on
that mountain to make the wind because we need the wind.
The wind keeps the air cool and clean. The wind brings the
clouds that give us rain to wash the Earth. The wind moves
the waters to keep them fresh and sweet. Without the wind,

life will not be good for us, for our children, or our children's children.

Gluscabi nodded his head. "Kaamoji, Grandmother," he said. "I understand."

Then he went outside. He faced in the direction from which the wind had once come and began to walk.

He walked through the fields and through the forests and the wind did not blow and he felt very hot. He walked through the valleys and up the hills and there was no wind and it was very hard for him to breathe. He came to the foothills and began to climb and he was very hot and sweaty indeed.

At last he came to the to the mountain where the Wind Eagle once stood and he went and looked down into the crevice. There was Wuchosen, the Wind Eagle, wedged upside down.

"Uncle?" Gluscabi called.

The Wind Eagle looked up as best he could. "Who calls me Uncle?" he said.

"It is Gluscabi, Uncle. I'm up here. But what are you doing down there?"

"Oh, Gluscabi," said the Wind Eagle, "a very ugly naked man with no hair told me that he would take me to the other peak so that I could do a better job of making the wind blow. He tied my wings and picked me up, but as he stepped over this crevice he dropped me in and I am stuck. And I am not comfortable here at all."

"Ah, Grandfath . . . er, Uncle, I will get you out."

Then Gluscabi climbed down into the crevice. He pulled the Wind Eagle free and placed him back on the mountain and untied his wings.

"Uncle," Gluscabi said, "it is good that the wind should blow sometimes and other times it is good that it should be still."

The Wind Eagle looked at Gluscabi and then nodded his head. "Grandson," he said, "I hear what you say."

So it is that sometimes there is wind and sometimes it is very still to this very day.

And so the story goes.

Love is something you and I must have. We must have it because our spirit feeds upon it. We must have it because without it we become weak and faint. Without love our self-esteem weakens. Without it our courage fails. Without love we can no longer look confidently at the world. We turn inward and begin to feed upon our own personalities, and little by little we destroy ourselves. With it we are creative. With it we march tirelessly. With it, and with it alone, we are able to sacrifice for others.

Chief Dan George

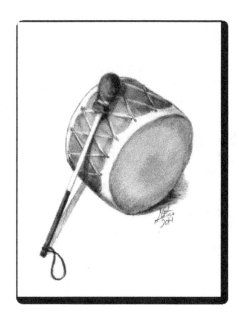

The Story of the Drum

(An Abenaki Legend)

It is said that when Creator was giving a place for all the spirits to dwell who would be taking part in the inhabitance of Mother Earth, there came a sound, a loud BOOM, from off in the distance.

As Creator listened, the sound kept coming closer and closer until it finally it was right in front of Creator. "Who are you?" asked Creator. "I am the spirit of the drum" was the reply. I have come here to ask you to allow me to take part in this wonderful thing." "How will you take part?" Creator questioned." I would like to accompany the singing of the people. When they sing from their hearts, I will to sing as though I was the heartbeat of Mother Earth. In that way, all creation will sing in harmony. "Creator granted the request, and from then on, the drum accompanied the people's voices.

Throughout all of the indigenous peoples of the world, the drum is the center of all songs. It is the catalyst for the spirit of the songs to rise up to the Creator so that the prayers in those songs reach where they were meant to go. At all times, the sound of the drum brings completeness, awe, excitement, solemnity, strength, courage, and the fulfillment to the songs. It is Mother's heartbeat giving her approval to those living upon her. It draws the eagle to it, who carries the message to Creator.

Hold on to what is good, even if it is a handful of dirt.
Hold on to what you believe, even if it is a tree that stands by itself.
Hold on to what you must do, even if it is a long way from here.
Hold on to life, even if it is easier to let go.
Hold on to my hand, even if I have gone away from you.

Pueblo Blessing

"Take only memories, Leave only footprints"

Chief Seattle (1780-1866)

Ghost of the White Deer

(Chickasaw)

A lore of the Chickasaw People of Oklahoma

A brave, young warrior for the Chickasaw Nation fell in love with the daughter of a chief. The chief did not like the young man, who was called Blue Jay. So the chief invented a price for the bride that he was sure that Blue Jay could not pay.

"Bring me the hide of the White Deer, : said the chief. The Chickasaws believed that animals that were all white were magical. "The price for my daughter is one white deer." Then the chief laughed. The chief knew that an all white deer, an albino, was very rare and would be very hard to find. White deerskin was the best material to use in a wedding dress, and the best white deer skin came from the albino deer.

Blue Jay went to his beloved, whose name was Bright Moon. "I will return with your bride price in one moon, and we will be married. This I promise you." Taking his best bow and his sharpest arrows Blue Jay began to hunt.

Three weeks went by, and Blue Jay was often hungry, lonely, and scratched by briars. Then, one night during a full moon, Blue Jay saw a white deer that seemed to drift through the moonlight. When the deer was very close to where Blue Jay hid, he shot his sharpest arrow. The arrow sank deep into the deer's heart. But instead of sinking to his knees to die, the deer began to run. And instead of running away, the deer began to run toward Blue Jay, his red eyes glowing, his horns sharp and menacing.

A month passed and Blue Jay did not return as he had promised Bright Moon. As the months dragged by, the tribe decided that he would never return.

But Bright Moon never took any other young man as a husband, for she had a secret. When the moon was shinning as brightly as her name, Bright Moon would often see the white deer in the smoke of the campfire, running, with an arrow in his heart. She lived hoping the deer would finally fall, and Blue Jay would return.

To this day the white deer is sacred to the Chickasaw People, and the white deerskin is still the favorite material for the wedding dress.

Race with Buffalo

(Cheyenne)

A story of the Cheyenne of the Great Plains

There was a time when all the animals lived in peace, when no one ate anyone else. All the animals were the same color, because they had not yet painted their faces.

Buffalo was the largest and strongest of the animals, and he was getting hungry, He wanted to be the chief of all the animals. He wanted to draw strength from all the other animals by eating their flesh. Buffalo wanted to become the eater of all the animals.

The Human People also said that they should become the chief of all the animals. People wanted to draw strength from all the other animals by eating their flesh. People wanted to become the eaters of all the other animals.

Buffalo challenged the Human People to a race, the winner of the race would become the chief of all the animals. The People said that they would accept such a challenge, but since buffaloes have four legs and People have only two, the People claimed the right to have another animal run the race in the People's place. The buffaloes consented.

The People chose the Bird People to represent them in the race. They chose Hummingbird, Meadowlark, Hawk, and Magpie. All the other animals and birds wanted to join the race, too, each of them thinking that just maybe they too had a chance to become chief of all the animals. All the animals took paint and painted the faces for the race, each according to his or her spiritual vision.

Skunk painted a white strip on himself and his symbol for the race. Antelope painted himself the color of the earth for the race. Raccoon painted black circles around his eyes and around his tail. Robin painted herself brown with a red breastplate.

The race was to be held at the edge of the Black Hills at the place known as Buffalo Gap. The competitors would race from the starting line sticks to the turn-around stick and then back to the starting line. All the animals, painted according to their vision, lined up between the sticks. Among the animals were the Bird People, who would run the race with their wings for the Human People, and Runs Slender Buffalo, the fastest runner of all the buffaloes.

The cry was given to begin and all the animals and birds set out on the race. Hummingbird took the lead, ahead of Runs Slender Buffalo, but his wings were so small that he soon fell behind. As the animals neared the turn-around stick, Runs Slender Buffalo took the lead. Then Meadowlark came up beside Runs Slender Buffalo, and the two went along side by side right into the turn. Runs Slender Buffalo wheeled around the stick, her hooves thundering, and she pulled away from Meadowlark, who went wide to make the turn.

The animals in the lead passed the late runners who were still headed for the stick. Meadowlark fell behind and cheered on Hawk as he passed her. Hawk gained on Run Slender Buffalo, and it looked like he might pass her. Her heart was pounding and her legs were tiring. But Hawk's wings were tiring also, and he soon fell behind.

Runs Slender Buffalo was nearing the finish line as the winner. It looked like the Buffalo People would become the eaters of all the animals!

Then, behind the buffalo woman, wings beating steadily, came Magpie. She was not a quick starter, but her wing-beats were hard and true. Her heart was strong. Her eyes did not wander form the finish line. She never looked back. Her wings were wide and she drove herself forward with beat after beat after beat. All the other animals had fallen behind. Runs Slender Buffalo looked over at the magpie, but the magpie never looked away from the starting sticks.

With each beat of her wings she moved past Runs Slender Buffalo by no more than the length of her bill. At the starting sticks, many animals began to line up to watch the finish. Raccoon, who had fallen out of the race early, had returned to the starting sticks. Now he stood up between the sticks and put out his little hands for the runners to touch as they passed. He would feel the touch of whoever was in the lead, and turn toward the winner.

Closer and closer came Runs Slender Buffalo, and some of the animals feared Raccoon would be trampled. Magpie gradually flew nearer to the ground so she could brush Raccoon's little hands as she flew past. Raccoon did not move, but stared straight at the onrushing pair. Magpie seemed to be pulling ahead. Runs Slender Buffalo leaned forward as she ran to touch Raccoon's hand with her great nose.

Magpie's wingtip touched Raccoon's little hand and he turned toward her and instant before Runs Slender Buffalo thundered past and he was surrounded by a great cloud of dust. All the animals waited breathlessly for the dust to settle. At last, there stood Raccoon with his little hand raised toward the path of Magpie.

The Human People had won the race!

The Buffalo wandered the great plains and ate grass and the people became the great hunters, the chief of all animals.

When all the trees have been cut down, when all the animals have been hunted, when all the waters are polluted, when all the air is unsafe to breathe, only then will you discover you cannot eat money.

Cree Prophecy

Mooin, the Bear's Child

Now in the Old Time there lived a boy called Sigo, whose father had died when he was a baby. Sigo was too young to hunt and provide food for the wigwam, so his mother was obliged to take another husband, a jealous spiteful man who soon came to dislike his small stepson, for he thought the mother cared more for the child than for himself. He thought of a plan to be rid of the boy.

"Wife," said he, "it is time the boy learned something of the forest. I will take him with me today, hunting."

"Oh no!" cried his wife. "Sigo is far too young!"

But the husband snatched the boy and took him into the forest, while the mother wept, for she knew her husband's jealous heart.

The stepfather knew of a cave deep in the forest, a deep cave that led into a rocky hill. To this cave, he led his stepson and told him to go inside and hunt for the tracks of rabbit. The boy hung back.

"It is dark in there. I am afraid."

"Afraid!" scoffed the man. "A fine hunter you'll make," and he pushed the boy roughly into the cave. "Stay in there until I tell you to come out."

Then the stepfather took a pole and thrust it under a huge boulder so that it tumbled over and covered the mouth of the cave completely. He knew well there was no other opening. The boy was shut in for good and would soon die of starvation.

The stepfather left the place, intending to tell the boy's mother that her son had been disobedient, had run off and got lost, and he had been unable to find him. He would not return home at once. He would let time pass, as if he had been looking for the boy. Another idea occurred to him. He would spend the time on Blomidon's beach and collect some of Glooscap's purple stones to take as a peace offering to his wife. She might suspect, but nothing could be proved, and nobody would ever know what had happened.

Nobody? There was one who knew already. Glooscap the Great Chief was well aware of what had happened and he was angry, very angry. He struck his great spear into the red stone of Blomidon and the clip split. Earth and stones tumbled down, down, down to the beach, burying the wicked stepfather and killing him instantly.

Then Glooscap called upon a faithful servant, Porcupine, and told him what he was to do.

In the dark cave in the hillside, Sigo cried out his loneliness and fear. He was only six after all, and he wanted his mother. Suddenly he heard a voice.

"Sigo! Come this way."

He saw two glowing eyes and went towards them, trembling. The eyes grew bigger and brighter and at last he could see they belonged to an old porcupine.

"Don't cry any more, my son," said Porcupine. "I am here to help you," and the boy was afraid no longer. He watched as Porcupine went to the cave entrance and tried to push away the stone, but the stone was too heavy. Porcupine put his lips to the crack of light between boulder and hill side and called out:

"Friends of Glooscap! Come around, all of you!"

The animals and birds heard him and came--Wolf, Raccoon, Caribou, Turtle, Possum, Rabbit, and Squirrel, and birds of all kinds from Turkey to Hummingbird.

"A boy has been left here to die," called the old Porcupine from inside the cave. "I am not strong enough to move the rock. Help us or we are lost."

The animals called back that they would try. First Raccoon marched up and tried to wrap his arms around the stone, but they were much too short. Then Fox came and bit and scratched at the boulder, but he only made his lips bleed. Then Caribou stepped up and, thrusting her long antlers into the crack, she tried to pry the stone loose, but only broke off one of her antlers. It was no use. In the end, all gave up. They could not move the stone.

"Kwah-ee," a new voice spoke. "What is going on?" They turned and saw Mooinskw, which means she-bear, who had come quietly out of the woods. Some of the smaller animals were frightened and hid, but the others told Mooinskw what had happened. She promptly embraced the boulder in the cave's mouth and heaved with all her great strength. With a rumble and a crash, the stone rolled over. Then out came Sigo and Porcupine, joyfully.

Porcupine thanked the animals for their help and said, "Now I must find someone to take care of this boy and bring him up. My food is not the best for him. Perhaps there is someone here whose diet will suit him better. The boy is hungry--who will bring him food ?"

All scattered at once in search of food. Robin was the first to return, and he laid down worms before the boy, but Sigo could not eat them. Beaver came next, with bark, but the boy shook his head. Others brought seeds and insects, but Sigo, hungry as he was, could not touch any of them, At last came Mooinskw and held out a flat cake made of blue berries. The boy seized it eagerly and ate.

"Oh, how good it is," he cried. And Porcupine nodded wisely.

"From now on," he said, "Mooinskw will be this boy's foster mother."

So Sigo went to live with the bears. Besides the mother bear, there were two boy cubs and a girl cub. All were pleased to have a new brother and they soon taught Sigo all their tricks and all the secrets of thee forest, and Sigo was happy with his new-found family. Gradually, he forgot his old life. Even the face of his mother grew dim in memory and, walking often on all fours as the bears did, he almost began to think he was a bear.

One spring when Sigo was ten, the bears went fishing for smelts. Mooinskw walked into the water, seated herself on her haunches and commenced seizing the smelts and tossing them out on the bank to the children. All were enjoying themselves greatly when suddenly Mooinskw plunged to the shore, crying, "Come children, hurry!" She had caught the scent of man. "Run for your lives!"

As they ran, she stayed behind them, guarding them, until at last they were safe at home.

"What animal was that, Mother?" asked Sigo.

"That was a hunter," said his foster-mother, "a human like yourself, who kills bears for food." And she warned them all to be very watchful from now on. "You must always run from the sight or scent of a hunter."

Not long afterwards, the bear family went with other bear families to pick blueberries for the winter. The small ones soon tired of picking and the oldest cub had a sudden mischievous thought.

"Chase me towards the crowd," he told Sigo, "just as men do when they hunt bears. The others will be frightened and run away. Then we can have all the berries for ourselves."

So Sigo began to chase his brothers towards the other bears, whooping loudly, and the bears at once scattered in all directions. All, that is, except the mother bear who recognized the voice of her adopted son.

"Offspring of Lox!" she cried. "What mischief are you up to now?" And she rounded up the children and spanked them soundly, Sigo too.

So the sun crossed the sky each day and the days grew shorter. At last the mother bear led her family to their winter quarters in a large hollow tree. For half the winter they were happy and safe, with plenty of blueberry cakes to keep them from being hungry. Then, one sad day, the hunters found the tree.

Seeing the scratches on its trunk, they guessed that bears were inside, and they prepared to smoke them out into the open.

Mooinskw knew well enough what was about to happen and that not all would escape.

"I must go out first," she said, "and attract the man's attention, while you two cubs jump out and run away. Then you, Sigo, show yourself and plead for your little sister. Perhaps they will spare her for your sake."

And thus it happened, just as the brave and loving mother bear had said. As soon as she climbed down from the tree, the Indians shot her dead, but the two male cubs had time to escape. Then Sigo rushed out, crying:

"I am a human, like you. Spare the she-cub, my adopted sister."

The amazed Indians put down their arrows and spears and, when they had heard Sigo's story, they gladly spared the little she-bear and were sorry they had killed Mooinskw who had been so good to an Indian child.

Sigo wept over the body of his foster mother and made a solemn vow.

"I shall be called Mooin, the bear's son, from this day forwards. And when I am grown, and a hunter, never will I kill a mother bear, or bear children!"

And Mooin never did.

With his foster sister, he returned to his old village, to the great joy of his Indian mother, who cared tenderly for the she-cub until she was old enough to care for herself.

And ever since then, when Indians see smoke rising from a hollow tree, they know a mother bear is in there cooking food for her children, and they leave that tree alone.

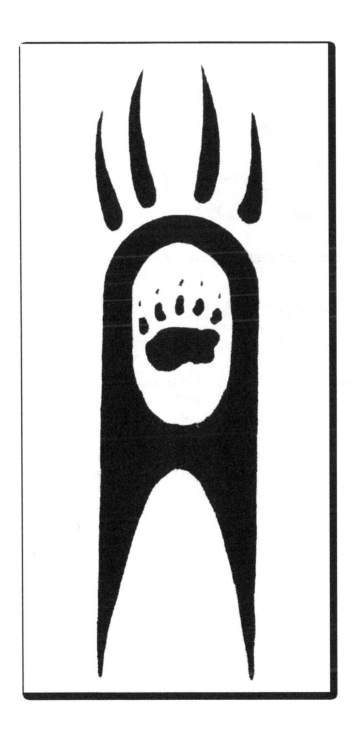

Bear Spirits

(A Winnebago (Hotcâk) Legend)

After Earthmaker created this island on which we live, he created all living things, man being the very last of these. The first and foremost animal that Earthmaker created was a bear of pure white color, whom he placed in the north. This is White Bear. The second bear that he created was Red Bear, whom he placed in the west. Earthmaker next created in the east a kind of grizzly bear Blue Bear, who was the color of the sky, either blue, or as some say, gray. The last bear created by Earthmaker was Black Bear, who was placed in the south. These four kinds of bears were created as Island Weights to help stop the incessant spinning of the primordial earth.

Spiritually, they were not only bears, but the four cardinal winds as well. White Bear was chief over polar bears, Red Bear held hegemony over the brown bears of earth, Blue Bear ruled over Grizzlies, and Black Bear was chief of the terrestrial black bears.

If the white man wants to live in peace with the Indian, he can live in peace. Treat all men alike. Give them all the same law. Give them all an even chance to live and grow. All men were made by the same Great Spirit Chief. They are all brothers. The Earth is the mother of all people, and all people should have equal rights upon it. Let me be a free man, free to travel, free to stop, free to work, free to trade where I choose my own teachers, free to follow the religion of my fathers, free to think and talk and act for myself, and I will obey every law, or submit to the penalty.

Native American Quote

Peace and happiness are available in every moment. Peace is every step. We shall walk hand in hand. There are no political solutions to spiritual problems. Remember: If the Creator put it there, it is in the right place. The soul would have no rainbow if the eyes had no tears.

Native American Quote

When we show our respect for other living things, they respond with respect for us.

Arapaho Proverb

Tipi Etiquette

Through research and many lists available, the following seems to be the best listing of etiquette that covers all Native American tribes. The source of the list is unknown and believed to be traditional.

When erecting a tipi, the door should always face East. This is where the Morning Star rises every morning.

If the door is open, a friend may enter the tipi directly. But if it is closed, he should announce his presence and wait for the owner to invite him to come in.

A male enters to the right and waits for the host to invite him to sit to the left of the owner at the rear.

If a woman enters a Tipi, she should enter after the man and must go to the left side.

Be hospitable.

Always assume your guest is tired, cold, and hungry.

Always give your guest the place of honor in the lodge and at the feast, and serve him in reasonable ways.

Invited guests are expected to bring their own bowls and spoons.

Never sit while your guests stand.

Woman never sit cross-legged like men. They can sit on their heels or with their legs to one side.

If your guests refuses certain foods, say nothing. He may be under vow.

Protect your guest as one of the family.

Do not trouble your guest with many questions about himself. He will tell you what he wants to know.

In another man's lodge, follow his customs-not your own.

Never worry your host with your troubles.

Always repay calls of courtesy. Do not delay.

Give your host a little present upon leaving. Little presents are little courtesies and never offend.

Say "thank you" for every gift, however small.

Compliment, even if you strain the facts to do so. However, it is rude to talk during a meal. Save your compliments for when you are leaving.

Never complement your host's possessions directly, for he then may feel obligated to give the object to you.

Never walk between persons talking.

Never interrupt persons talking.

Always give place to your seniors in entering or leaving the lodge, or anywhere.

Never sit while your seniors stand.

Never force your conversations on anyone.

Speak softly, especially before your elders, or in the presence of strangers.

Younger men remained silent until they were invited to speak.

Never come between anyone and the fire.

Do not stare at strangers. Drop your eyes if they stare hard at you; above all for women.

The women of the lodge are the keepers of the fire, but the men should help with the heavier sticks.

Be kind and generous with those less fortunate.

Show respect to all men and women, but grovel to none.

Let silence be your motto, until duty bids you to speak. Pause to gather your thoughts before speaking. Never speak in haste.

Thank the Great Spirit for every meal.

When the host cleaned his pipe, that was a signal to leave.

When meetings were held by Plains Indians, everyone sat in a circle to indicate harmony and connectedness. A Talking Stick would be passed to the right (clockwise) to indicate the direction the sun travels, and only the person who held the stick could talk. The stick was and still is a symbol of respect for the thoughts and the stories of each member of the circle. All others in the circle were expected to sit quietly and engage in active listening. No one interrupted while the person holding the Talking Stick was speaking. When the person holding the Talking Stick was finished speaking, it was handed to the next person in the circle. If that person chose to not speak, the stick was then handed to the next person until everyone in the circle had participated. Anything could be used as a Talking Stick as long as it had personal meaning.

The Quill-Work Girl and Her Seven Brothers

A Cheyenne Legend

Hundreds of years ago there was a girl who was very good at quill work, so good that she was the best among all the tribes everywhere. Her designs were radiant with color, and she could decorate anything -- clothing, pouches, quivers, even tipi's.

One day this girl sat down in her parents' lodge and began to make a man's outfit of white buckskin -- war shirt, leggings, moccasins, gauntlets, everything. It took her weeks to embroider them with exquisite quill work and fringes of buffalo hair marvelous to look at. Though her mother said nothing, she wondered. The girl had no brothers, nor was a young man courting her, so why was she making a man's outfit?

As if life wasn't strange enough, no sooner had she finished the first outfit than she began working on a second, then on a third. She worked all year until she had made and decorated seven complete sets of men's clothes, the last a very small one. The mother just watched and kept wondering. At last after the girl had finished the seventh outfit, she spoke to her mother. "Someplace, many days' walk from here, lives seven brothers," she said. "Someday all the world will admire them. Since I am an only child, I want to take them for my brothers, and these clothes are for them."

"It is well, my daughter," her mother said. "I will go with you."

"This is too far for you to walk," said the girl.

"Then I will go part of the way," said her mother.

They loaded their strongest dogs with the seven bundles and set off toward the north. "You seem to know the way," said the mother.

"Yes, I don't know why, but I do," answered the daughter.

"And you seem to know all about these seven young men and what makes them stand out from ordinary humans."

"I know about them," said the girl, "though I don't know how."

Thus they walked, the girl seeming sure of herself. At last the mother said, "This is as far as I can go." They divided the dogs, the girl keeping two for her journey, and took leave of each other. Then the mother headed south back to her village and her husband, while her daughter continued walking into the north.

At last the daughter came to a lone, painted, and very large tipi which stood near a wide stream. The stream was shallow and she waded across it, calling: "It is I, the young-girl-looking-for-brothers, bringing gifts."

At that a small boy about ten years old came out of the tipi. "I am the youngest of seven brothers," he told the girl. "The others are out hunting buffalo, but they'll come back after a while. I have been expecting you. But you'll be a surprise to my brothers, because they don't have my special gifts of `No Touch'."

"What is the gift of no touch?" asked the girl.

"Sometime you'll find out. Well, come into the tipi."

The girl gave the boy the smallest outfit, which fitted him perfectly and delighted him with its beautiful quill work.

"I shall take you all for my brothers," the girl told him.

"And I am glad to have you for a sister," answered the boy.

The girl took all the other bundles off her two dogs' backs and told them to go back to her parents, and at once the dogs began trotting south.

Inside the tipi were seven beds of willow sticks and sage. The girl unpacked her bundles and put a war shirt, a pair of leggings, a pair of moccasins, and a pair of gauntlets upon each of the older brothers' beds. Then she gathered wood and built a fire. From her packs she took dried meat, choke cherries, and kidney fat, and cooked a meal for eight.

Toward evening just as the meal was ready, the six older brothers appeared laden with buffalo meat. The little boy ran outside the lodge and capered, kicking his heels and jumping up and down, showing off his quilled buckskin outfit.

"Where did you get these fine clothes?" the brothers asked.

"We have a new sister," said the child. "She's waiting inside, and she has clothes for you too. She does the most wonderful quill work in the world. And she's beautiful herself!"

The brothers greeted the girl joyfully. They were struck with wonder at the white buckskin outfits she had brought as gifts for them. They were as glad to have a sister to care for as she was to have brothers to cook and make clothes for. Thus they lived happily.

One day after the older brothers had gone out to hunt, a light-colored buffalo- calf appeared at the tipi and scratched and knocked with his hoof against the entrance flap. The boy came out and asked it what it wanted.

"I am sent by the buffalo nation," said the calf. "We have heard of your beautiful sister, and we want her for our own."

"You can't have her," answered the boy. "Go away."

"Oh well, then somebody bigger than I will come," said the calf and ran off jumping and kicking its heels.

The next day when the boy and the sister were alone again, a young heifer arrived, lowing and snorting, rattling the entrance flap of the tipi.

Once more the child came out to ask what she wanted.

"I am sent by the buffalo nation," said the heifer. "We want your beautiful sister for ourselves."

"You can't have her," said the boy. "Go away!"

"Then somebody bigger than I will come," said the heifer, galloping off like the calf before her.

On the third day a large buffalo cow, grunting loudly, appeared at the lodge. The boy came out and asked, "Big buffalo cow, what do you want?"

"I am sent by the buffalo nation," said the cow. "I have come to take your beautiful sister. We want her."

"You can't have her," said the boy. "Go away!"

"Somebody very big will come after me," said the buffalo cow, "and he won't come alone. He'll kill you if you don't give him your sister." With these words the cow trotted off.

On the fourth day the older brothers stayed home to protect the girl. The earth began to tremble a little, then to rock and heave. At last appeared the most gigantic buffalo bull in the world, much larger than any you see now. Behind him came the whole buffalo nation, making the earth shudder. Pawing the ground, the huge bull snorted and bellowed like thunder. The six older brothers, peering out through the entrance hole, were very much afraid, but the little boy stepped boldly outside. "Big, oversized buffalo bull, what do you want from us?" he asked.

"I want your sister," said the giant buffalo bull. "If you won't give her to me, I'll kill you all."

The boy called for his sister and older brothers to come out. Terrified, they did so.

"I'll take her now," growled the huge bull.

"No," said the boy, "she doesn't want to be taken. You can't have her. Go away!"

"In that case I'll kill you now," roared the giant bull. "I'm coming!"

"Quick, brother, use your special medicine!" the six older brothers cried to the youngest.

"I am using it," said he. "Now all of you, catch hold of the branches of this tree. Hurry!" He pointed to a tree growing by the tipi. The girl and the six brothers jumped up into its branches. The boy took his bow and swiftly shot an arrow into the tree's trunk, then clasped the trunk tightly himself. At once the tree started to grow, shooting up into the sky in no time at all. It all happened much, much quicker than it can be told.

The brothers and the girl were lifted up in the tree branches, out of reach of the buffalo. They watched the herd of angry animals grunting and snorting, milling around the tree far below.

"I'll chop the tree down with my horns!" roared the giant buffalo. He charged the tree, which shook like a willow and swayed back and forth. Trying not to fall off, the girl and the brothers clutched the branches. The big bull had gouged a large piece of wood from the trunk.

The little boy said, "I'd better use one more arrow." He shot another arrow high into the treetop, and again the tree grew, shooting up another thousand feet or so, while the seven brothers and the girl rose with it.

The giant buffalo bull made his second charge. Again his horns stabbed into the tree and splintered wood far and wide. The gash in the trunk had become larger.

The boy said, "I must shoot another arrow." He did, hitting the treetop again, and quick as a flash the tree rose another thousand feet.

A third time the bull charged, rocking the tree, making it sway from side to side so that the brothers and the girl almost tumbled out of their branches. They cried to the boy to save them. The child shot a fourth arrow into the tree, which rose again so that the seven young men and the girl disappeared into the clouds. The gash in the tree trunk had become dangerously large.

"When that bull charges again, he will shatter this tree," said the girl. "Little brother, help us!"

Just as the bull charged for the fourth time, the child let loose a single arrow he had left, and the tree rose above the clouds.

"Quick, step out right on the clouds. Hurry!" cried the little boy. "Don't be afraid!"

The bull's head hit the tree trunk with a fearful impact. His horns cut the trunk in two, but just as the tree slowly began to topple, the seven brothers and the girl stepped off its branches and into the sky.

There the eight of them stood. "Little brother, what will become of us now? We can never return to earth; we're up too high. What shall we do?"

"Don't grieve," said the little boy, "I'll turn us into stars."

At once the seven brothers and the girl were bathed in radiant light. They formed themselves into what the white men call the Big Dipper. You can see them there now. The brightest star is the beautiful girl, who is filling the sky with glimmering quill work, and the star twinkling at the very end of the Dipper's handle is the little boy. Can you see him?

The Flying Canoe

A Passamaquoddy Legend

Beside a beautiful lake not far from the sea, there lived three brothers. They were young rivals, each trying to do everything better than the others.

Sometimes they were visited by an old woman. She was nearly blind so crippled that she could hardly walk, and always hungry. But when she had eaten some food, she could do wonderful things, and she could give remarkable power to a person she liked.

Joseph, the youngest of the three young men, treated her very well. Whenever he gave her food, she was grateful. One day after he had fed her, she said to him, "Take your axe and make some moccasins for yourself--some wooden ones. In them you will be able to run as fast as a bird."

And so Joseph made for himself a pair of wooden moccasins. When he wore them, he could run very fast. In fact, he could run faster than the swiftest animals. He caught game animals and brought home much meat.

His two brothers were jealous because the youngest was a more skillful hunter. They wondered what he had been doing, and they watched him continually. One day they saw him open his birch-bark box and take out his wooden moccasins. Then he disappeared.

The brothers had already noticed certain curious chips where Joseph had been working. So they were very glad when they saw what he took from his box. They gathered together all the wood chips and made moccasins for themselves. In their wooden moccasins they could run even faster than Joseph.

Then Joseph knew that they had learned his secret.

The next time the old woman came for food, he fed her as usual. This time she said, as she thanked him, "Make for yourself a dugout canoe. Then you shall soar across the water like a bird."

So Joseph made a dugout canoe. Using it on the lake, he caught big fish and many birds. Again his brothers were jealous, and again they watched him in all that he did. Finding some chips after he had made his boat, the two older brothers gathered them and built a canoe for themselves. Working together, they made it better than Joseph's. It was a wonderful canoe. In it they went out to sea and speared many whales.

This time Joseph was angry. He called the old woman and fed her well, giving her more food than ever before.

"Now you will make another canoe," she said when she had eaten. "This one will fly in the air. You will really fly like a bird."

And so Joseph made another dugout. When he had finished making it, he carefully picked up all the chips and burned them. Then he took leave of his brothers and sailed off in the air.

He saw many strange lands and many strange people below him. He passed over high mountains and rivers and lakes. He passed over oceans. At last, after much journeying through the air, and after many adventures in other lands, Joseph returned home. There he lived in peace.

Míkmaq Legend of the Wild Goose

A Micmac Legend

When birds migrated to the south in the long, long ago, they came and left by themselves. Many of the little ones were killed by storms. This caused great sorrow to Kluskap, the great God of the Míkmaq. He asked the Wild Goose the largest bird and the last one to leave the north each fall, to care for all of the smaller ones. The Wild Goose called all the little birds together and told them of Kluskap's wonderful plan.

They agreed that the Wild Goose would lead them in their long flight to the south, shelter them in their far away homes, be with them during their journey back and protect them while they were in the North during the summer season.

Ever since the time of Kluskap the Wild Goose has been the guide and protector of all the small birds that come to our country each year.

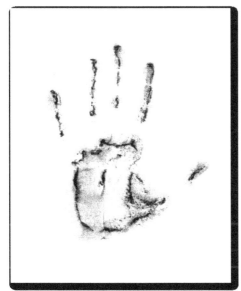

The Porcupine Quills

Menomi

Some Indian women, who had once befriended Manabush, went to him. They wanted some porcupine quills. With them they wished to ornament some garments. He gladly promised to try to get them. He traveled through the forests and over the hills to find Porcupine. They were friends. When he found him he told him of his mission. But Porcupine refused to give away any of his quills. Neither would he exchange any for anything which Manabush could offer. He was going to a dance and ceremony and needed all of the quills he had.

Manabush was determined to have some of the quills. He said he was very hungry and asked Porcupine if he had a kettle. Manabush gathered various edible herbs of which his friend was very fond and could produce sleep. Porcupine ate heartily of the meal and fell asleep. While he was asleep Manabush drew a lot of fine quills from his body and went away. The women were greatly pleased with the quills. They flattened and dyed them in bright colors. When Porcupine later visited the Indian camp he saw all of the women wearing buckskin garments, beautifully ornamented with porcupine quills. He was suspicious, but too late.

We, the great mass of the people think only of the
love we have for our land, we do love the land
where we were brought up. We will never let our hold
to this land go, to let it go it will be like throwing
away (our) mother that gave (us) birth.

Letter from Aitooweyah to John Ross,
Principal Chief of the Cherokees.

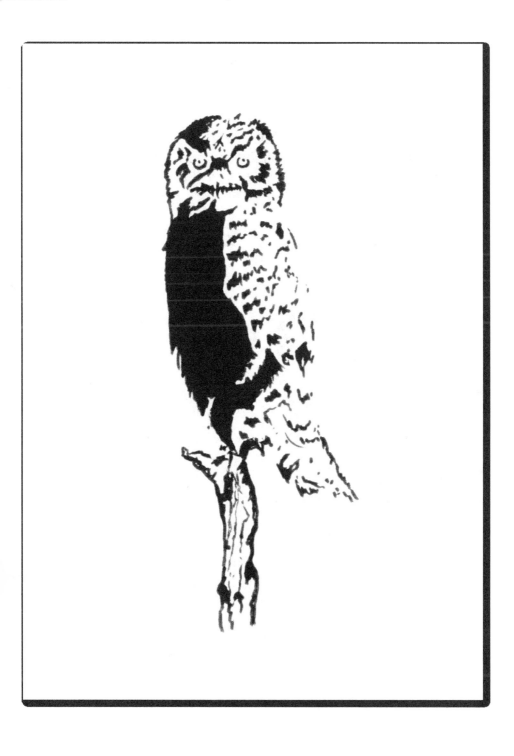

Why The Owl Has Big Eyes

Iroquois

Raweno, the Everything-Maker, was busy creating various animals. He was working on Rabbit, and Rabbit was saying: "I want nice long legs and ears like a deer, and sharp fangs and claws like a panther."

"I do them up the way they want to be; I give them what

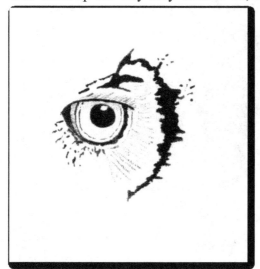 they ask for," said Raweno. He was working on Rabbit's hind legs, making them long, the way Rabbit had ordered.

Owl, still unformed, was sitting on a tree nearby waiting his turn. He was saying: "Whoo, whoo, I want a nice long neck like Swan's, and beautiful red feathers like Cardinal's, and a nice long beak like Egret's, and a nice crown of plumes like Heron's. I want you to make me into the most beautiful, the fastest, the most wonderful of all the birds."

Raweno said: "Be quiet. Turn around and look in the other direction. Even better, close your eyes. Don't you know that no one is allowed to watch me work?" Raweno was just then making Rabbit's ears very long, the way Rabbit wanted them

Owl refused to do what Raweno said. "Whoo, whoo," he replied, "nobody can forbid me to watch. Nobody can order me to close my eyes. I like watching you, and watch I will."

Then Raweno became angry. He grabbed Owl, pulling him down from his branch, stuffing his head deep into his body, shaking him until his eyes grew big with fright, pulling at his ears until they were sticking up at both sides of his head.

"There," said Raweno, "that'll teach you. Now you won't be able to crane your neck to watch things you shouldn't watch. Now you have big ears to listen when someone tells you what not to do. Now you have big eyes--not so big that you can watch me, because you'll be awake only at night, and I work by day. And your feathers won't be red like cardinal's, but gray like this" --and Raweno rubbed Owl all over with mud--"as punishment for your disobedience." So Owl flew off, pouting: "Whoo, whoo, whoo."

Then Raweno turned back to finish Rabbit, but Rabbit had been so terrified by Raweno's anger, even though it was not directed at him, that he ran off half done. As a consequence, only Rabbit's hind legs are long, and he has to hop about instead of walking and running. Also, because he took fright then, Rabbit would have been an altogether different animal.

As for Owl, he remained as Raweno had shaped him with anger--with big eyes, a short neck, and ears sticking up on the sides of his head. On top of everything, he has to sleep during the day and come out only at night.

How the Fawn Got Its Spots

A Dakota Sioux Legend

Long ago, when the world was new, Wakan Tanka, The Great Mystery, was walking around. As he walked he spoke to himself of the many things he had done to help the four-legged ones and the birds survive.

"It is good," Wakan Tanka said. "I have given Mountain Lion sharp claws and Grizzly Bear great strength; it is much easier now for them to survive.

"I have given Wolf sharp teeth and I have given his little brother, Coyote, quick wits; it is much easier now for them to survive.

"I have given Beaver a flat tail and webbed feet to swim beneath the water and teeth which can cut down the trees and I have given slow-moving Porcupine quills to protect itself. Now it is easier for them to survive.

"I have given the Birds their feathers and the ability to fly so that they may escape their enemies. I have given speed to the Deer and the Rabbit so that it will be hard for their enemies to catch them. Truly it is now much easier for them to survive."

However, as Wakan Tanka spoke, a mother Deer came up to him. Behind her was her small Fawn, wobbling on weak new legs.

"Great One," she said. "It is true that you have given many gifts to the four-leggeds and the winged ones to help them survive. It is true that you gave me great speed and now my enemies find it hard to catch me. My speed is a great protection, indeed. But what of my little one here? She does not yet have speed. It is easy for our enemies, with their sharp teeth and their claws to catch her. If my children do not survive, how can my people live?"

"Wica yaka pelo!" said Wakan Tanka. "You have spoken truly; you are right. Have your little one come here and I will help her."

Then Wakan Tanka made paint from the earth and the plants. He painted spots upon the fawn's body so that when she lay still her color blended in with the earth and she could not be seen. Then Wakan Tanka breathed upon her, taking away her scent.

"Now," Wakan Tanka said, "your little ones will always be safe if they only remain still when they are away from your side. None of your enemies will see your little ones or be able to catch their scent."

So it has been from that day on. When a young deer is too small and weak to run swiftly, it is covered with spots that blend in with the earth. It has no scent and it remains very still and close to the earth when its mother is not by its side. And when it has grown enough to have the speed Wakan Tanka gave its people, then it loses those spots it once needed to survive.

We are now about to take our leave and kind farewell to our native land, the country the Great Spirit gave our Fathers, we are on the eve of leaving that country that gave us birth, it is with sorrow we are forced by the white man to quit the scenes of our childhood...we bid farewell to it and all we hold dear.

Charles Hicks, Tsalagi (Cherokee) Vice Chief speaking of The Trail of Tears, Nov. 4, 1838

The Gifts Of The Little People

An Iroquois Legend

There once was a boy whose parents had died. He lived with his uncle who did not treat him well. The uncle dressed the boy in rags and because of this the boy was called Dirty Clothes.

This boy, Dirty Clothes, was a good hunter. He would spend many hours in the forest hunting food for his lazy uncle who would not hunt for himself.

One day Dirty Clothes walked near the river, with two squirrels that he had shot hanging from his belt. He walked near the cliffs which rose from the water. This is where the Little People, the Jo-Ge-Oh, often beat their drums. Most of the hunters from the village were afraid to go near this place, but Dirty Clothes remembered the words his mother had spoken years ago, "Whenever you walk with good in your heart, you should never be afraid."

A hickory tree grew there near the river. He saw something moving in its branches. A black squirrel was hopping about high up in the top of the tree. When Dirty Clothes heard a small voice. "Shoot again, Brother," the small voice said. "You still have not hit him."

Dirty Clothes looked down and there near his feet were two small hunters. As he watched, one of them shot an arrow but it fell short of the black squirrel. "Ah," Dirty Clothes thought, "they will never succeed like that. I must help them." He drew his bow and with one shot brought down the squirrel.

The tiny hunters ran to the squirrel. "Whose arrow is this?" asked one of them. They looked up and saw the boy. "Eee-yah," said one of the tiny hunters, "you have shot well. The squirrel is yours."

"Thank you," Dirty Clothes answered, "but the squirrel is yours and also these others I have shot today."

The two small hunters were very glad. "Come with us," they said. "Come visit our lodge so we can thank you properly."

Dirty Clothes thought about his uncle, but it was still early in the day and he could hunt some more after visiting them. "I'll come with you," Dirty Clothes said.

The two Little People led the boy to the river. There a tiny canoe was waiting, only as big as one of his shoes, but his friends told him to step inside. He took one step... and found he had become as small as the tiny hunters and was sitting with them inside their canoe.

The Little People dipped their paddles and up the canoe rose into the air! It flew above the hickory tree, straight to the cliffs and into a cave, the place where the Jo-Ge-Oh people lived. There the two hunters told their story to the other Little People gathered there who greeted the boy as a friend. "You must stay with us." his new friends said, "for just a short time so we can teach you."

Then the Jo-Ge-Oh taught Dirty Clothes things which he had never known. They told him many useful things about the birds and the forest animals. They taught him much about the corn and the squash and the beans which feed human life. They taught him about the strawberries which glow each June like embers in the grass and showed him how to make a special drink which the Little People love.

Last they showed him a new dance to teach his people, a dance to be done in a darkened place so the little People could come and dance with them unseen, a dance which would honor the Jo-Ge-Oh and thank them for their gifts.

Four days passed and the boy knew that the time had come for him to leave. "I must go to my village," he told his friends.

So it was that with the two small hunters he set out walking towards his home. As they walked with him, his two friends pointed to the many plants which were useful and the boy looked at each plant carefully, remembering its name. Later, when he turned to look back at his friends, he found himself standing all alone in a field near the edge of his village.

Dirty Clothes walked into his village wondering how so many things had changed in just four days. It was the same place, yet nothing was the same. People watched him as he walked and finally a woman came up to him. "You are welcome here, Stranger," said the woman. "Please tell us who you are."

"Don't you know?" he answered. 'I am Dirty Clothes."

"How can that be?" said the woman. "Your clothing is so beautiful."

At that, he saw his old rags were gone. The things he wore now were of fine new buckskin, embroidered with moose hair and porcupine quills. "Where is my uncle," he asked the woman, "the one who lived there in that lodge and had a nephew dressed in rags?"

Then an old man spoke up from the crowd. "Ah," said the old man, "that lazy person? He's been dead many years and why would a fine young warrior like you look for such a man?"

Dirty Clothes looked at himself and saw he was no longer a boy. He had become a full-grown man and towered over the people of his village. "I see," he said, "the Little People have given me more gifts than I thought." And he began to tell his story.

The wisest of the old men and women listened well to this young warrior. They learned many things by so listening. That night all his people did the Dark Dance to thank the Jo-Ge-Oh for their gifts and, in the darkness of the lodge, they heard the voices of the Little People joining in the song, glad to know that the human beings were grateful for their gifts. And so it is, even to this day, that the Little People remain the friends of the people of the long-house and the Dark Dance is done, even to this day.

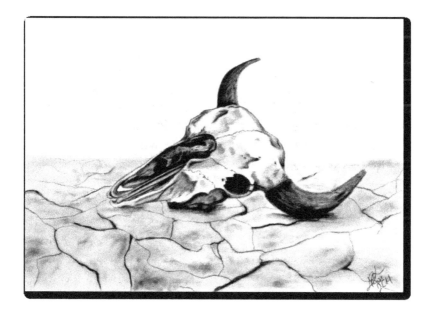

One Stick, Two Sticks

An American Indian Legend - Nation Unknown

An old man is dying, and calls his people to his side. He gives a short, sturdy stick to each on his many offspring, wives, and relatives. "Break the stick," he instructs them. With some effort, they all snap their sticks in half. "This is how it is when a soul is alone without anyone. They can be easily broken."

The old man next gives each of his kin another stick, and says, "This is how I would like you to live after I pass. Put your sticks together in bundles of twos and threes. Now, break these bundles in half." No one can break the sticks when there are two or more in a bundle. The old man smiles. "We are strong when we stand with another soul. When we are with another, we cannot be broken."

Cherokee Blessing

May the warm winds of Heaven blow softly on your home,
And the Great Spirit bless all who enter there.
May your moccasins make happy tracks in many snows,
And may the rainbow always touch your shoulder.

Bear Did Not Always Hibernate

An American Indian Legend - Nation Unknown

The bear is a giant of a beast, but gentle to all who see its tender loving ways. The bear did not always sleep (hibernate).

It was during the time of the first winter that Wind gave Bear the gift of sleep. All the animals of the forest thought Bear was lazy and slow. They would tease him and harass the poor soul daily. They viewed his kind gentle ways as a weakness.

They always laughed at his friends, and when he stopped and talked to them. Still Bear did not hate or get angry at the animals who made fun of him, he just smiled and went on his way. He loved his feathered friends, his underground friends and his underwater friends. The only time he was sad is when he was hungry and had to eat one of them.

One day father Wind heard all the animals talking about how foolish bear was. Even Fish turned against his friend. This made Wind very mad.

In a dream he taught Bear what plants to eat and all about the bad things Fish had said. He told Bear fish was not a friend but food. He also told Bear that because he was kind he would receive a special gift. Then bear awoke wondering what gift would Wind give him.

In the next dream, Bear was sad. Winter asked him what is wrong? "I am only good because I have good friends". "That is true", said Winter. So he told Bear to go and tell all his friends about the gift that Wind had promised him.

When Bear awoke he ran through the forest and told all who would listen. This made him very tired and sleepy so he went back to cave and fell asleep.

As before, many creature did not listen to Bear. They went about their business. Some even called him crazy. So Winter decided to teach them a lesson. As Bear and his friends slept, flew away, or gathered food, without knowing Winter came down upon the forest. Yet, he made sure that those who were friends of Bear were not aware of him or his brother Wind. To them it was a time of the gift.

So as Winter begins his journey across the land, one can still see who were the friends of Bear...Are You???

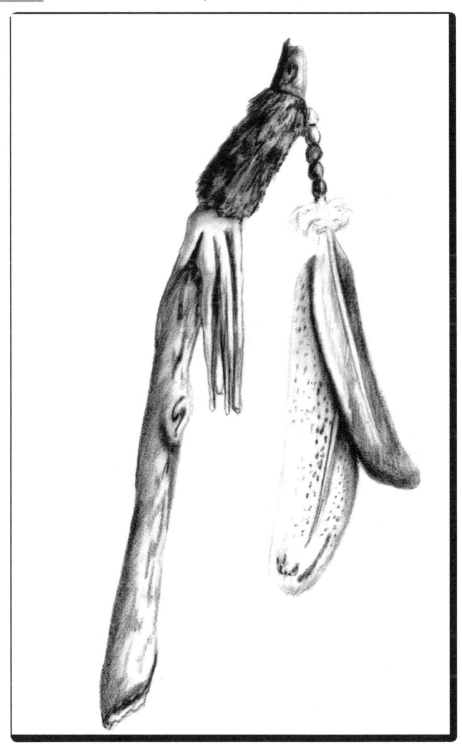

Traditional Talking Stick

The Talking Stick is a tool used in many Native American Traditions when a council is called. It allows all council members to present their Sacred Point of View. The Talking Stick is passed from person to person as they speak and only the person holding the stick is allowed to talk during that time period.

The Answering Feather is also held by the person speaking unless the speaker addresses a question to another council member. At that time, the Answering Feather is passed to the person asked to answer the query. Every member of the meeting must listen closely to the words being spoken, so when their turn comes, they do not repeat unneeded information or ask impertinent, questions.

Indian children are taught to listen from age three forward; they are also taught to respect another's viewpoint. This is not to say that they may not disagree, but rather they are bound by their personal honor to allow everyone their Sacred Point of View. People responsible for holding any type council meeting are required to make their own Talking Stick. The Talking Stick may be used when they teach children, hold council, make decisions regarding disputes, hold Pow-Wow gatherings, have storytelling circles, or conduct a ceremony where more than one person will speak.

Since each piece of material used in the Talking Stick speaks of the personal Medicine of the stick owner, each Talking Stick will be different. The Qualities of each type of Standing Person (Tree) brings specific Medicine. White Pine is the Peace Tree, Birch symbolizes truth, Evergreens represent the continued growth of all things. Cedar symbolizes cleansing. Aspen is the symbol for seeing clearly since there are many eye shapes on the truth. Maple represents gentleness. Elm is used for wisdom; Mountain Ash for protection; Oak for strength; Cherry for expression, high emotion, or love. Fruit woods are for abundance and walnut or pecan for gathering of energy or beginning new projects.

Each person making a Talking Stick must decide which type of Standing Person (Tree) will assist their needs and add needed medicine to the Councils held. The ornamentation of each stick all have meaning.

In the Lakotah Tradition, red is for life, yellow is for knowledge, blue is for prayer and wisdom, white is for spirit, purple is for healing, orange is for feeling kinship with all living things, black is for clarity and focus. The type of feathers and hide used on a Talking Stick are very important as well. The Answering Feather is usually an Eagle Feather, which represents high ideals, truth as viewed from the expansive eye of the eagle, and the freedom that comes from speaking total truth to the best of one's ability.

The Answering Feather can also be the feather of a Turkey, the Peace Eagle of the south, which brings peaceful attitudes as well as the give and take necessary in successful completion of disputes.

In the Tribe that see Owl as good Medicine, the Owl feather may also be used to stop deception from entering the Sacred Space of the Council.

The skins, hair or hides used in making a Talking Stick brings the abilities, talents, gifts and medicine of those creatures-beings to council in a variety of ways. Buffalo brings abundance; Elk brings physical fitness and stamina;

deer brings gentleness; rabbit brings the ability to listen with big ears; the hair from a horse's tail or mane brings perseverance and adds connection to the earth and to the spirits of the wind.

If an illness of heart, mind, spirit, or body has affected the group gathering, snake skin may be wrapped around the Talking Stick so that healing and transmuting of those poisons can occur. The Talking Stick is the tool that teaches each of us to honor the Sacred Point of View of every living creature.

----Eastern Band of Cherokee Indians ---enrollment # 1009

<u>Other Titles Available From G.W. Mullins And C.L. Hause</u>
Walking With Spirits Native American Myths, Legends, And Folklore
Volumes One Thru Six

The Native American Cookbook

Native American Cooking - An Indian Cookbook With Legends And Folklore

The Native American Story Book - Stories Of The American Indians For Children
Volumes One Thru Five

The Best Native American Stories For Children

Cherokee A Collection of American Indian Legends, Stories And Fables

Creation Myths - Tales Of The Native American Indians

Strange Tales Of The Native American Indians

Spirit Quest - Stories Of The Native American Indians

Animal Tales Of The Native American Indians

Medicine Man - Shamanism, Natural Healing, Remedies And Stories Of The Native
American Indians

Native American Legends: Stories Of The Hopi Indians
Volumes One and Two

Totem Animals Of The Native Americans

The Best Native American Myths, Legends And Folklore
Volumes One Thru Three

Ghosts, Spirits And The Afterlife In Native American Indian Mythology And
Folklore

The Native American Art Book – Art Inspired By Native American Myths And
Legends

For information about the book and novel releases of
G.W. Mullins please visit his web site at
http://gwmullins.wix.com/officialsite

All images contained in this book are original works by
C.L. Hause. For more information on his art and other projects
please visit his web page at *http://clarencehause.wix.com/homepage*

CPSIA information can be obtained
at www.ICGtesting.com
Printed in the USA
LVHW092004161120
671835LV00005B/1001